How To Know

THE
AQUATIC
PLANTS

Pictured Key
Nature Series

How To Know

THE
AQUATIC
PLANTS

G. W. Prescott

University of Montana Biological Station

WM. C. BROWN COMPANY PUBLISHERS
Dubuque, Iowa

THE PICTURED-KEY NATURE SERIES

How To Know The—

Printed in United States of America

PREFACE

With the ever-mounting interest in water quality and quantity there is more and more attention being directed toward aquatic biota. The importance of the roles that algae and higher plants play in the water realm cannot be overemphasized, and it is because of the current interests in aquatic plants that this synopsis was prepared. The following illustrated key to genera was written for those who may not be experienced botanists, but who wish an introduction to the plants of the water world and to know their names.

In the United States there are about 1,300 species of aquatic or semi-aquatic plants in some 306 genera and representing about 65 families. These numbers include many species which may be only incidentally present in moist or marshy situations and are subject to the definitive limitations drawn by respective botanists who have written on such plants. Some 165 of these genera are included in the synoptic key to follow wherein an attempt has been made to include mostly the truly aquatic plants and those which are characteristically and commonly present in bogs, marshes and along the shore line.

As is usual with all such keys there are limitations and problems. One which is inherent in a key that is written with the objectives of the following develops because of the variability among species constituting a genus. Hence, in many instances there is no single character that clearly differentiates one genus from another. Therefore the reader is asked to consider a combination of characteristics to classify a plant in which he is interested. Also, the problem is met in part by keying out a genus in more than one place according to different characters. Many statements in the choices used in the following key are somewhat extended to more fully characterize a genus. The reader is urged to refer to other less abridged works if he is interested in species determinations.

Each genus is illustrated and for some more than one species is depicted to help give an idea of the variations within a genus. The illustrations were prepared from living specimens whenever possible. Others have been drawn (and sometimes stylized) from herbarium specimens. The author is grateful to Dr. W. C. Vinyard for his help in inking many of the drawings and is indebted to several colleagues who have read the manuscript.

Whenever appropriate the economic or biological importance of respective genera are pointed out in the descriptive notes. The family relationship for each genus is given with the illustration, and a checklist of aquatic plant families and their representation is appended. The illustrated glossary-index should assist in understanding the descriptive terms used in the key.

v

INTRODUCTION

Who cares anything about aquatic plants? What are the reasons for studying them and learning their names? Anyone who fishes, swims or boats in lakes and lagoons is well-aware that water vegetation is often obnoxiously abundant. One sometimes wonders what the plants are, where they came from and what could be done to eradicate them. It is necessary to know the habits and peculiarities of aquatic plants and the conditions which determine their distribution if one wishes to regulate their growth. In this connection, as well as for other reasons, it is desirable to know the names of the plants. Although troublesome in many instances, aquatic vegetation plays many important roles in the biology of the water realm, and in addiiton has a number of economic importances.

For example, aquatic animals, as well as some terrestrial or semi-terrestrial ones such as moose and muskrat, use water plants for food. Both aquatic and upland birds obtain much of their food from them. Further, plants of shallow water and the shore offer cover and nesting sites to many kinds of birds. Fish also use aquatics directly for food, or they feed upon the small animals that live on and around aquatic plants. Some kinds of fish (sunfish, perch) have their nests in beds of aquatic plants. Many aquatic insects live on and in plants, spending all or part of their life history here, using them for food, for egg-laying or for emergence.

Not a few species of aquatic plants are directly important to man economically. Indian Rice, Water Chestnut and Delta Potato for example are sources of food. In some parts of the world the bulrush is used for the building of boats or for floor mats, partitions, etc. Of indirect value are the roles that aquatic plants play in bank erosion, in beach building and in the filling in of marshes and bogs. In fact aquatic plants constitute one of the most important agencies in the ageing of lakes, leading eventually to their extinction. A few aquatic plants bring about the deposition of lime thus, after a long period of time, produce useful marl deposits.

In addition to these relationships it must be recalled that aquatic plants have a bearing on limnology and that there are many inter-actions between plants, water chemistry and bottom deposits. Further, students of plant morphology, physiology and plant evolution find aquatic plants of great interest. Most plants in the water have about the same relationship to terrestrial ones that aquatic mammals such as whales have to land animals. They are representative of evolutionary series of plants which, after having developed on land, have become adjusted to and have returned to an aquatic abode. The morphological

vii

and physiological changes required to meet the problems of an aquatic existence invite scientific studies.

Most of the reasons for studying aquatic plants require that one give attention also to many species which are semi-aquatic or marginal. Further, the same interests demand that one consider other than the larger, more obvious flowering plants. Several of the larger algae are important in the same ways that are the flowering plants. A few bryophytes and several pteridophytes are found in an aquatic flora. Further, the same species may be both aquatic and terrestrial, or a terrestrial species may have aquatic varieties. Hence it is difficult if not impossible to delimit "aquatic plants."

The divisions (Phyla) and subgroups (Classes) which comprise the plant kingdom are listed for reference. Those groups which are considered in this work are indicated by (*).

   I. Chlorophyta (Green Algae)*
   II. Euglenophyta (Euglenoid Algae)
   III. Chrysophyta (Yelow-green Algae)
   IV. Cryptophyta (Chrysophyte Algae)
   V. Pyrrhophyta (Dinoflagellate Algae)
   VI. Cyanophyta (Blue-green Algae)
   VII. Phaeophyta (Brown Algae)
   VIII. Rhodophyta (Red Algae)*
   IX. Chloromonadophyta (Chloromonad Algae)
   X. Bryophyta
        A. Hepaticae (Liverworts)*
        B. Musci (Mosses)*
   XI. Psilopsida (Psilophyte Ferns)
   XII. Lycopsida (Club Mosses)
   XIII. Sphenopsida (Horse Tail Ferns)*
   XIV. Pteropsida (Ferns)*
   XV. Spermatophyta (Seed Plants)*
        A. Gymnospermae*
        B. Angiospermae*
            1. Monocotyledonae*
            2. Dicotyledonae*

When all the aquatic plant species are placed in review it is noteworthy that a majority are in the Monocotyledonae of the seed plants, although more of the genera are in the Dicotyledonae (primarily because there are more dicot genera in nature than monocot). Further, it is noted that of the families which are entirely aquatic in the United States, 6 are monocot and only 2 are dicots. These families are indicated in the checklist of genera which is appended.

CONTENTS

WHAT IS A SPECIES?

By way of explanation for the inexperienced reader, a species is a population of organisms which are similar or identical. Thus, one of the yellow water lilies is an example of a species and all similar water lilies bear the specific epithet *advena*, for example. There are other yellow water lilies which are in general similar but which consistently vary enough to be recognizably different and so are called by another specific name, *variegata*, for example. The yellow water lilies which have much in common are apparently related and they are included together to constitute a genus, *Nuphar*. Thus we have *Nuphar advena*, *N. variegata*, *N. polysepala* and others. The genus and species name together constitute the scientific name of an organism; thus we have the binomial system of nomenclature.

We have in the same pond perhaps water lilies which seem to have much in common with the yellow water lily (such as general stem and leaf characters and embryo anatomy) but which are clearly not the same in outsanding respects such as shape of flower, number of petals, form of fruit, etc. There are several species of white or lotus-like water lilies which comprise the genus *Nymphaea* such as *N. odorata*, *N. tuberosa*, etc. *Nymphaea* and *Nuphar* are obviously related so these two genera (with all their species) and other genera with somewhat similar characteristics are grouped into a family, the Nymphaeaceae. Here would be classed *Nelumbo*, the yellow lotus, and *Brasenia*, the water shield, and others. Families of organisms which have some characteristics in common are often grouped to form Orders, the Orders comprise Classes and Classes comprise Phyla or Divisions. The botanist refers to these groupings (species, genus, etc.) as taxa (singular taxon).

HOW TO USE THE KEY

The following key is the dichotomous type, that is, two choices are presented and one must decide which of the statements applies to a specimen in question. Having made a selection, one follows the numbers through the succeeding choices, eventually arriving at a genus name. If one does not reach a satisfactory conclusion it is necessary to return to a previously considered dichotomy which offers some alternatives and follow through on another series of choices. In a number of instances the key leads to the same genus name in more than one place. This is necessary because the genus may include species which are variable in respect to a character used in the key statements. It will be noted that in so far as possible vegetative characters are used in presenting choices. When final separation cannot be concluded by using these characters, flower and/or reproductive features are employed in the key. Characteristics which must be considered are:

1. Whether true leaves and stem are present.
2. Leaf shape.
3. Type of leaf margin.
4. Whether the leaf is simple or compound.
5. Arrangement of leaves on the stem.
6. Presence of ligule.
7. Presence of stipules.
8. Presence of sheaths (some leaves occur only as sheaths at the base of the stem).
9. Form of flowers. (See text figures 1-5 illustrating some flower types.)
10. Arrangement and location of flowers; type of inflorescence.

Text Fig. 1. Diagram of a grass flower. l, Lemma; o, Ovary; p, Palea; r, Rachilla; s, Stigma; st, Stamen.

2

Text Fig. 2. Diagram of a grass spikelet. g, Glumes.

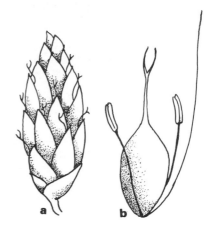

Text Fig. 3. Inflorescence of the Cyperaceae, diagrammatic. a, Spikelet; b, Perfect flower with pistil and stamens.

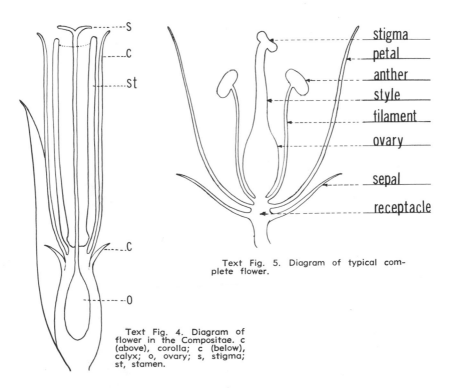

stigma
petal
anther
style
filament
ovary

sepal
receptacle

Text Fig. 5. Diagram of typical complete flower.

Text Fig. 4. Diagram of flower in the Compositae. c (above), corolla; c (below), calyx; o, ovary; s, stigma; st, stamen.

3

DISTRIBUTION OF AQUATIC PLANTS

Aquatic plant species, like most aquatic organisms, are more widely distributed than terrestrial. This is mostly so because factors or conditions to which aquatic plants adjust are, in general, more uniform than on land. Water temperature, water chemistry and life-giving nutrients are less variable. Yet species are selective of their habitat, so much so that a combination of species often can be used as an index of the physical-chemical nature of a habitat. Whereas perhaps most species thrive well in and often require organic bottom sediments, others are adapted to sandy bottoms. Many are capable of growing in deep water where light is subdued, and do not need to reach the surface (some *Potamogeton*, e.g.). Plants like *Sagittaria* and *Alisma* begin their development submersed but most species of these genera become emergent for full reproduction. Plants such as *Elodea*, although anchored in shallow water, do not emerge except to place their flowers at the surface. Some species (*Myriophyleum*) are highly sensitive to intense light (even when under water where light is relatively not strong) whereas others must grow so as to obtain maximum illumination.

The majority of aquatic plants are found in water well-supplied with electrolytes such as calcium and magnesium carbonate, usually in accompaniment with nitrates and phosphates. In such waters the flora is rich both in quantity and in number of species. But genera such as *Isoetes Utricularia*, *Nitella* and *Nymphaea* include species which can live in soft or acid waters, sometimes in darkly stained bog lakes. Oxygen supply is often critical for some plants and not a few are confined to well-aerated waters such as rapidly flowing streams. (*Podostemum*, *Fontinalis* spp.).

A few aquatic plants occur in salt water and are found only there or in highly brackish and saline situations inland from the sea (*Zostera*, *Salicornia*, e.g.).

To all these types of habitats aquatic plants make their adjustment by their morphological and physiological characteristics, and by their reproductive habits. Leaves of many species are finely divided, thus increasing the absorbing surface for gasses and for light. Some have modified or highly divided roots which aid in oxygen uptake (*Trapa*, e.g.). Flotation is achieved by the development of canals in petiole and stem (*Myriophyleum*, *Elodea*), and these also serve as gas reservoirs. *Oenanthe*, a genus requiring ample oxygen, has tufts of epidermal hairs which increase the uptake of gasses. The difficulty of obtaining light for photosynthesis is frequently met by having chloroplasts in the epidermis as well as in the mesophyll of the leaf, a character not found in land plants. Another compensation for the same problem is by having unusually broad leaf surfaces exposed to light, as in the water lily family, an extreme example being the Amazonian water lily *Victoria regia* with peltate leaves several feet across.

4

COLLECTING AQUATIC PLANTS

Aquatic plants which are deeply submersed must be collected by a raking tool, or by an especially constructed "plant hook." Such a tool can be made very simply by running 3 or 4 doubled strands of heavy wire through a 10-inch section of 1½-inch pipe. The doubled strands should be about 2 feet long. The loops of the doubled strands are twisted together to form an eye-hole. The free ends of the wire are then bent back to form an anchor-like hook. A small amount of solder or melted lead can be poured into the pipe to keep the wires in position and to give weight to the hook. In the twisted knot of wires a small but strong rope or heavy cord is tied, about 35 to 40 feet usually being suitable (depending upon the depth of water to be sampled). The plant hook is tossed from shore or from a boat and dragged along the bottom to grapple the plants. Specimens can be carried to the laboratory in pails or tubs. A simple method is to use ordinary plastic bags (garbage bags in rolls obtained at the grocery store are ideal). Small collections or individual specimens can be kept fresh and unbroken for quite some time when placed in such bags with just enough water to bathe the roots and to maintain suitable humidity.

It is often desirable to examine plants in the field to determine flower and fruit characters, stipules, etc. For this a 14 X or 20 X doublet handlens is needed. The collector is reminded to have the handlens safely tied around the neck and to have the plant hook affixed to the boat when working over water.

Either before or after making identification of plants they may be prepared as herbarium specimens. Erect and/or firm plants may be placed in folded newspaper and plant driers as are terrestrial species. Submersed plants and those with flexible, drooping, tangled and highly divided leaves are best cared for by placing them directly on herbarium paper under water. For this 12 x 18-inch baking pans are suitable. The specimen is first rinsed and washed of extraneous material and dead leaves. Then it is placed in a pan of clean water. A sheet of herbarium paper supported on a 11 x 15-inch sheet of zinc or firm aluminum can then be slipped under the specimen. With tweezers and needles the specimen can be floated and spread on the paper in a life-like position, the various parts being arranged so as to show taxonomic features clearly. The metal sheet and its paper can then be slowly removed by sliding it back and up out of the water and placed in a semi-vertical position to drain. After all excess water has been drained away the sheet with its specimen can then be placed in a folded newspaper. The newspaper is placed between blotters and ventilators and put to press. If the specimen is especially wet, or thick and matted, a small sheet of muslin can be laid over the specimen between the newspaper. Plants with especially thick stems and dense root masses should be split or divided. Also large flowers such as the yellow water lily (*Nuphar*) should be halved in addition to an uncut flower. If specimens are mucilaginous a sheet of plastic may be spread over them before placing between blotters.

It may be desirable or of interest to collect dry fruits and/or seeds to be used in identifying and comparing seeds of plants used as food by birds and animals. After drying, seeds are packaged in small envelopes and can be filed, or affixed to the herbarium sheet.

KEY TO THE GENERA OF AQUATIC PLANTS

1a. Plants with true leaves, or true stem and (usually) roots; floating or rooted; aquatic, or on shore...............................23

1b. Plants without true leaves, stem and roots (although rootlets are present on some thalloid duckweeds); plants with small (2 to 8 mm long) "leaves" as in the mosses, e.g.; a lobed thallus as in the liverworts; or plants filamentous.........................2

2a. Plants thalloid, sometimes dichotomously lobed (liverworts); plants with joints or flat lobes, or minute globular thalli (duckweeds); plants without an elongate axis with branches or scales (See, however, *Dermatocarpon*, a thalloid, aquatic lichen not included here)..3

2b. Plants otherwise; filamentous (algae), or with elongate axes bearing small, scalelike "leaves" (mosses)........................10

3a. Plants floating (sometimes incidentally stranded on mud); rootlets present or absent..5

3b. Plants attached, growing on moist substrates, with rhizoids forming a mat along a midrib on the ventral side..................4

4a. Thallus a lobed, flattened, dorsiventral, leaflike expansion, with saucerlike gemmae cups on the upper surface; when mature, with sex organs borne on stalked gametophores which are disclike (male) or palm treelike (female) arising from notches in the thallus (Liverworts). Fig. 1..*Marchantia*

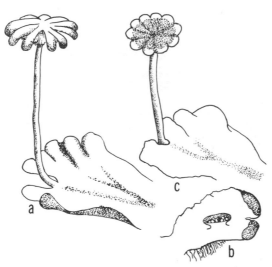

Fig. 1. *Marchantia polymorpha* (Marchantiaceae) a. Portion of thallus showing an archegoniophore (female branch); b. A young thallus with cupule and gemmae buds; c. Portion of a thallus with antheridiophore (male branch).

This liverwort is dioecious, that is the female and male reproductive organs are borne on separate plants. Before maturity the plants bear small cups on the dorsal surface in which special regenerative buds (gemmae) are produced. *Marchantia* is found on stream banks, on logs and rocks, or in swamp margins. It is a pioneer on denuded soils or on ash after a bog fire. The species shown here is nearly world-wide in its distribution.

4b. **Thallus a flattened, leaflike expanse without saucerlike gemmae cups; when mature with a stalked, female gametophore distinctly coneshaped at the apex. Fig. 2**.....................*Conocephalum*

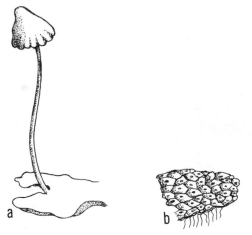

Plants occur in much the same habitat as *Marchantia;* differ in the prominence of the areolae on the dorsal surface, and in the shape of the disc which bears the archegonia, being conical rather than lobed. Also this genus lacks the cupules and gemmae buds. *Conocephalum* has a faint spicy odor.

a

b

Fig. 2. *Conocephalum conicum* (Marchantiaceae) a. Portion of thallus showing an archegoniophore (female branch) with its cone-shaped head on the under side of which archegonia are produced; b. Portion of thallus showing the raised areolae in which their is a breathing pore.

5a. (3) Plants without rootlets....................................7

5b. Plants with rootlets...6

6a. Thallus composed of 2 or a few, circular joints, up to 3.5 mm wide, which are purple on the under side, the joints showing about 7 indistinct nerves, with several rootlets from each joint (Great Duckweed). Fig. 3..*Spirodela*

Fig. 3. *Spirodela polyrhiza* (Lemnaceae) Habit showing a variety of shapes of joints. Note the several rootlets borne on each joint.

This duckweed is the largest in the Lemnaceae. It forms surface "meadows" in quiet water and is readily identified by the purple underside of the lobes and by the numerous rootlets. *Spirodela* is important as a wild fowl food plant and often is so abundant as to become a nuisance.

6b. Thallus composed of oval, circular, or elongate-forked joints, 2 to 4 mm across, with 1 to 3 radiating nerves, not purple on the under side, with only 1 rootlet from each joint (Duckweed). Fig. 4.. ....*Lemna*

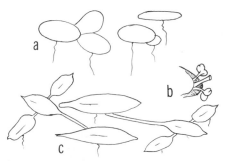

Fig. 4. *Lemna* (Lemnaceae) a. *Lemna minor;* b. Marginal flower of *Lemna minor;* c. *Lemna trisculca.*

This genus is perhaps the most common and abundant of all the duckweeds, especially *L. minor* which forms extensive surface mats in quiet waters and in slowly flowing streams. It is a useful index organism of hardwater habitats. The plants proliferate rapidly by budding and often present a nuisance. *L. valdiviana* has oblong rather than oval joints. *L. trisculca* has spatulate joints that form T-shaped or cross-shaped arrangements. The plants float in tangled clumps beneath the surface. Each joint of *Lemna* bears a single, threadlike rootlet.

9

7a. (5) Plants formed of one or more minute, elongate, bandlike or flattened thalli 4 to 8 mm long, arranged in a star-shaped cluster, the cluster usually floating just beneath water surface (Strap-shaped Duckweed). Fig. 5..*Wolffiella*

This curiously-shaped plant has a finger-like or strap-shaped thallus that often occurs in stellate clusters; has no roolets. The plant is widely distributed in eastern and southern United States.

Fig. 5. *Wolffiella floridana* (Lemnaceae) Habit.

7b. Thalli shaped otherwise......................................8

8a. Plants composed of minute globules, or subspherical, granular bodies, 2 mm or less in diameter (Water Meal). Fig. 6.......*Wolffia*

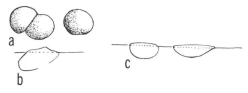

The minute thalli in this genus are the smallest flowering plants in the world. They occur as green grains at or near the surface of quiet waters. Tiny flowers are borne on the margins of the grains. These species are probably more widely distributed than indicated by present records because they are so easily overlooked in aquatic situations, intermingled as they are with other species of Lemnaceae and with *Ricciocarpus natans*. *Wolffia punctata* is the most commonly found. The thallus is flattened on the under side; has dark spots.

Fig. 6. *Wolffia* (Lemnaceae) a. *Wolffia columbiana;* b. *Wolffia papulifera;* c. *Wolffia punctata.*

8b. Thalli shaped otherwise......................................9

9a. Thallus, a narrow, flattened dichotomously lobed ribbon, often with a few white rhizoids from the ventral surface (Liverworts). Fig. 7. . . . .*Riccia*

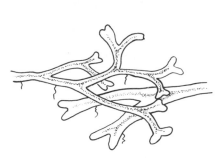

This thalloid liverwort may be either aquatic or epiphytic on trees in humid forests (especially in the tropics). Species may also occur on logs and fallen wood in northern latitudes. *Riccia fluitans* is a dichotomously divided ribbon; occurs in clumps in marginal waters of lakes and sloughs. There are few or no rhizoids. The plants are useful as duck food; are widely distributed.

Fig. 7. *Riccia fluitans* (Ricciaceae).

9b. Thallus lumpy, or moundlike, with dichotomously lobed margins; numerous, dark purple scales from the ventral surface (Liverwort) Fig. 8. . . . .*Ricciocarpus*

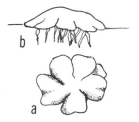

Fig. 8. *Ricciocarpus natans* (Ricciaceae) a. Vertical view of a thallus; b. Lateral view showing ventral scales.

This species is mostly aquatic and floating but may be found stranded on mud. The dichotomously lobed mounds are grooved above and have dark-colored, purplish scales from the lower surface. The plants may be abundant in favorable, quiet habitats and become important in aquatic biology, especially as food for birds.

10a. (2) Thalli filamentous, threadlike; branching usually very evident. 11

10b. Thalli with leaflike lobes or joints, or with small (3 to 8 mm long) scalelike "leaves" arranged along a "stem" (Mosses). 15

11a. Main filament somewhat rigid; plants growing erect from the bottom of aquatic habitats, with branches at definite nodes; plants macroscopic, 3 cm to as much as 1 M in length. 12

11b. Thalli with limp, lax axes. 14

11

12a. Plants gray-green (usually) because of lime deposits (gritty to the touch), with a skunk-like odor; most species with axes enclosed by overlying, cortical or columnar cells (seen with a hand lens); nodes with whorls of branches ("leaves") all the same length (Chlorophyta; Muskgrass, Stonewort) Fig. 9 . . . . *Chara*

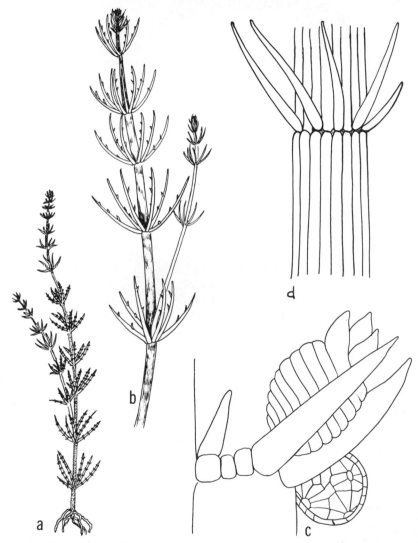

Fig. 9. *Chara* sp. (Characeae) a. Habit of plant showing whorls of short branches at the nodes, and the basal rhizoids; b. Anterior portion of a plant showing short branches of limited growth and one branch with unlimited growth; c. A node of a branch on which an oogonium (nucule) and an antheridium (globule) are borne; d. Section of a "stem" showing cortical cells. See Fig. 9d.

12b. Plants without lime, usually dark green; without a disagreeable odor; no over-lying cortical cells 13

13a. Branches, especially those bearing reproductive structures dichotomously or trichotomously forked at the tips; branches of uniform length, in whorls at the nodes. Fig. 10 .... *Nitella*

Members of this genus are more delicate and greener than *Chara* often is, and have no disagreeable odor. Plants are uncorticated and do not deposit lime on the exterior. They usually occur in soft water with a low pH.

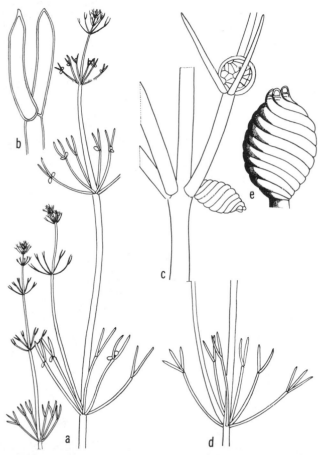

Fig. 10. *Nitella* sp. (Characeae) a. Habit of anterior portion of thallus showing bifurcations at the tips of the branches; b. Cells at the apex of a branch; c. A section of a branch with an oogonium (nucule) below and an antheridium above, borne vertically in the furcations; d. A species with trifurcate branch tips; e. Oogonium with 10 cells in the coronula.

13b. Branches not divided or forked at the tip; some branches at the nodes short, others much elongated and threadlike; reproductive structures in heads of short branches. Fig. 11.........*Tolypella*

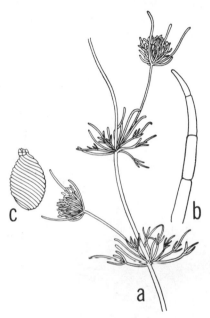

This is a relative of *Nitella*, with but a few species and more limited in distribution. *Tolypella* can be identified by its scraggly appearance resulting from the irregular branch lengths, some being very long and threadlike. Numerous short branches form clumps in which the reproductive structures are borne. Species may be either dioecious or monoecious.

Fig. 11. *Tolypella* (Characeae) a. Habit of plant portion showing the rather dense heads of short branches on which the sex organs are produced; b. Tip of a branch; c. An oogonium showing the divisions of the cells in the coronula.

14a. (11) Thallus arbuscular (treelike), embedded in soft, amorphous mucilage, with whorls of branches at definite nodes, producing a "beaded" effect; plants gray-violet, tawny or buff-colored, (Rhodophyta). Fig. 12..............................*Batrachospermum*

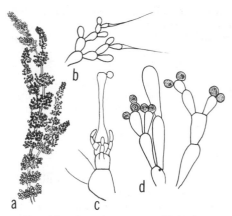

This fresh-water red alga forms highly gelatinized, bushy tufts in either flowing water or in pools. There is very little phycoerythrin hence the plants are gray-green, violet-green or tawny. Large specimens in the tropics may be two feet in length, but usually the thallus is a short, tufted growth on rocks and sticks. Whorls of branches give a beaded effect, reminding one of strings of frog eggs, hence the name *Batracho* (frog) *Sperm* (seeds).

Fig. 12. *Batrachospermum* (Batrachospermaceae) a. Habit of anterior portion of plant showing beaded effect produced by whorls of short branches at nodes; b. Branch tip showing pyriform cells and apical hairs; c. A carpogonial branch with a spermatium fused with the trichogyne of the carpogonium; vegetative branches from the lower cells of the carpogonial branch; d. Apices of branches bearing spermatangia.

14b. Thallus a truft of repeatedly branched filaments, forming a bushy growth, without whorls of out-turned branches; not embedded in mucilage; plants green (Chlorophyta). Fig. 13....... .... *Cladophora*

This genus occurs mostly as a bushy tufted green alga, attached to rocks and wood in flowing water, on dams and in waterfalls. But some species are found abundantly in lakes, especially on wave-washed shores. Growth is profuse in hardwater situations and when plants become free-floating they may cause considerable nuisance when they are washed onto beaches as tangled, decaying, ropy masses.

Fig. 13. *Cladophora* (Cladophoraceae). Habit of anterior portion of branched filament; cells with netlike or fragmented chloroplast.

15

15a. (10) Thallus attached, terrestrial or submersed, with small, leaf-like scales or lobes arranged along a short or long "stem" plants sometimes becoming disattached) (Mosses)............16

15b. Thallus floating, with round, oval or elongate joints or leaflike lobes, not arranged on an elongate "stem" (Water Ferns; Lemnaceae) 20

16a. Plants in bogs, green or pale green (sometimes tipped with red); stems erect with radially arranged branches which are closely clustered near the top where they form a rosette; stem and branches (some drooping) clothed by small, overlapping "leaves" (Bog Moss). Fig. 14................................*Sphagnum*

This is the familiar bog moss, often light green because most of the plant body is composed of empty, colorless cells. Species may occur on margins of soft-water lakes, in acid soils and in meadows, sometimes at high altitudes if there is an abundance of moisture. Also *Sphagnum* may form mats around the margins of hard-water, calcareous lakes contributing to the "quaking bog" that encroaches on the lake. Species are differentiated by details of leaf morphology. Some such as *S. magelanicum* and *S. rubellum* are reddish in the upper branches. This moss is economically important as peat, as a packing material, as a conditioner for horticultural soils and in the preparation of surgical bandages.

Fig. 14. *Sphagnum* (Sphagnaceae) a. Habit of upper portion of a gametophore showing decurrent and upwardly directed branches; b. A mature sporophyte at the tip of a branch.

16b. Plants not as above.................................17

17a. Thallus prostrate, composed of an axis with deep, lateral lobings which nearly form leaflike expansions; plants mostly terrestrial in moist habitats (Leafy Liverwort). Fig. 15. . . . . *Chiloscyphus*

This liverwort has a thallus in which a branched axis gives rise bilaterally to deep lobes which are leaflike; belongs to the Leafy Liverworts of the Jungermanniales. Plants are found on stones in cold, running water.

Fig. 15. *Chilo-scyphus* (Harpan-thaceae) Portion of a prostrate thallus.

17b. Thallus otherwise; plants aquatic 18

18a. "Leaves" forming three rows along the "stem," closely overlapping, without a midrib (Moss). Fig. 16 . . . . *Fontinalis*

There are several species of this moss (Bryales) which are aquatic. *F. antipyretica* is perhaps the most common, a dark green and relatively large species, occurring on rocks in swiftly running water. The leaves are somewhat trough-shaped, closely overlapping, have no midrib. Such mosses are of biological significance since they harbor aquatic insects, larvae and other microbiota.

Fig. 16. *Fontinalis* (Fontinalaceae) a. Anterior portion of a branch with closely overlapping, rather rigid leaves; b. Leaves with dorsal keel; c. Single leaves.

18b. "Leaves" spreading and curled, either in 2 rows along the "stem" or spiral...19

19a. "Leaves" in 2 rows spreading from two sides of the "stem," with a midrib and a secondary small plate of cells forming a lateral pocket at the base (Moss). Fig. 17.....................*Fissidens*

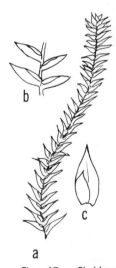

This is a sprawling moss with elongate-elliptic leaves that spread from two sides of the stem. There is a midrib and a plate of superficial cells on one side at the base. Several species occur in both lakes and streams, attached to and covering rocks and twigs.

Fig. 17. *Fissidens* (Fissidentaceae) a. Anterior portion of a branch showing leaves arranged on two sides; b. leaf arrangement; c. single leaf showing the secondary flap of cells at the base.

19b. "Leaves" spirally arranged, arising from 3 sides of the "stem," with a midrib (Moss). Fig. 18................... *Drepanocladus*

In this genus the leaves are spirally arranged, curled, and have a midrib. Species usually grow profusely, forming dense mats on submersed wood, on lake bottoms, sometimes floating in extensive clumps. Biologically they are important as oxygenators and as primary producers on lakes which cannot support aquatic vegetation, especially soft-water lakes low in nutrients.

Fig. 18. *Drepanocladus* (Hypnaceae) a. A branch showing curling lateral branches; b. A single leaf showing sickle shape.

20a. (15) Leaves small, (3 to 4 mm) smooth, oval, closely arranged on a short stem, each leaf having a ventral lobe that bears a sporocarp when mature; leaves usually tinged with red (Water Velvet, an aquatic fern). Fig. 19........................ *Azolla*

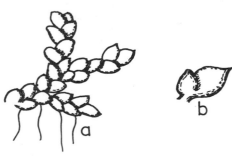

This is called Water Velvet, a small, aquatic fern which grows so densely as to form surface mats, often tinged with red. The plant has a short stem giving rise bilaterally to rows of overlapping, scalelike leaves that have a ventral, submersed lobe. *A. caroliniana* is the common species in North America; is biologically important as food for aquatic birds.

Fig. 19. *Azolla* (Salviniaceae) a. Thallus with small overlapping leaves and rootlets; b. Single leaf showing thumblike ventral lobe.

20b. Plants otherwise 21

21a. Leaves circular, bilobed, 2 or 4 from a short stem and bearing stiff bristles on the upper surface; lower submersed leaves finely dissected, appearing like roots, bearing sporocarps; roots lacking (Water Fern; Floating Moss). Fig. 20 . . . . *Salvinia*

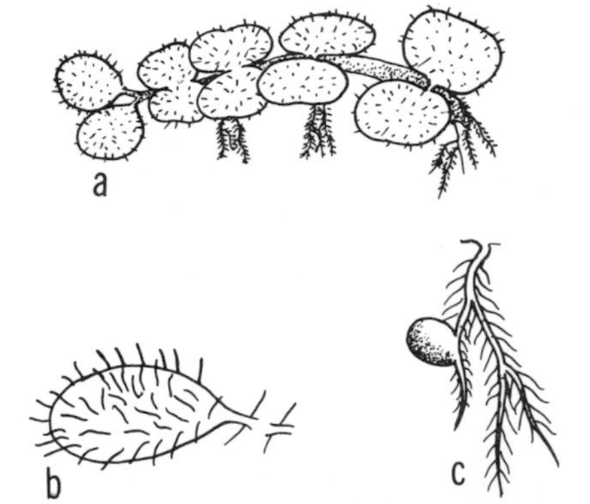

Fig. 20. *Salvinia* (Salviniaceae) a. A portion of a stem showing circular floating, dorsal leaves and the finely divided, submersed ventral leaves; b. A single leaf blade with stiff trichomes; c. Ventral leaf with a sporocarp.

Whereas some tropical species of this genus of aquatic fern may have larger leaves, those which occur in the United States have leaves 1 to 1.5 cm across when mature. Besides the two rows of dorsal leaves there are finely dissected ventral and submersed leaves that have the appearance of roots, but the plant has no roots. The leaves arise 3 at a node. In the tropics, species of *Salvinia* may become so dense as to clog barge canals and to interfere with navigation. *Salvinia* is much-used as an aquarium plant.

21b. Plants otherwise 22

22a. Thallus with a pair of floating, leaflike lobes, purple on the under side, with several roots from each lobe or joint (Great Duckweed). Fig. 3 . . . . *Spirodela*

22b. Thallus with oval, rounded or spatula-shaped lobes or joints, with 1 rootlet per joint; thallus not purple on the under side. Fig. 4 . . . . *Lemna*

23a. (1) Plants semi-woody vines, woody shrubs or trees; semi-aquatic. 24

23b. Plants herbaceous, annual or perennial, sometimes with persistent, semi-woody stems..................................36

24a. Leaves needlelike; coniferous trees with deciduous leaves (*)..25

24b. Leaves broad, with or without a petiole.....................26

25a. Needles angular in cross section, several in a cluster or fascicle (Larch, Tamarack). Fig. 21.............................*Larix*

Although not usually thought of as an aquatic plant tamarack or larch occurs in bogs and acid situation along with *Sphagnum*, cranberry, leather-leaf, pitcher plants and sundew. The trees, usually not more than 25 or 30 feet high, have soft needlelike leaves in fascicles which become yellow and drop away each fall.

Fig. 21. *Larix laricina* (Pinaceae) Twig showing fascicled, needlelike leaves.

(*)*Picea mariana* or Black Spruce (evergreen) has leaves borne singly from all sides of the stem. The needles are angular in cross section and stiff. Dwarfed trees grow in northern bogs often with Tamarack and associated plants.

25b. Needles flat, borne singly from two sides of the stem; twigs flat
(Bald Cypress). Fig. 22.............................. *Taxodium*

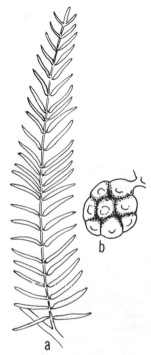

Bald Cypress is an inhabitor of swamps in southeastern United States where there are extensive, but rapidly disappearing stands. It is more nearly an aquatic than *Larix* because the trees grow in the water of swamps and river margins, sending up the familiar cypress knees which facilitate oxygen uptake. Galls develop on the twigs and these, falling into the water, are used by aquatic birds for food.

Fig. 22. *Taxodium distichum* (Pinaceae) a. Twig, leaf shape and arrangement; b. Carpellate cone.

26a. (24) Plants with semi-woody stems; perennial............... 27

26b. Plants definitely woody; trees and shrubs................... 29

27a. Plant a creeping vine in *Sphagnum* bogs or in peaty soil (Cranberry). Fig. 23...*Vaccinium*

Cranberry is a creeping, semi-woody vine inhabiting *Sphagnum* bogs, or as *V. macrocarpon* is grown commercially in acid soil. Like many other members of the Ericaceae species are confined to acid situations.

Fig. 23. *Vaccinium oxycoccus* (Ericaceae) Portion of procumbent stem with a flower.

27b. Plants erect...28

28a. Stems semi-woody, with a spongy base; leaves tapered at the base to a short petiole, opposite, but occasionally in 3's and rarely alternate on the same stem; plants marginal, the branches

23

drooping and sprawling over the water (Water Willow). Fig. 24. .
. . . . *Decodon*

Water Willow is important as a builder of lake margins. Dense stands sometimes occupy a marshy area, or there may be isolated clumps in shallow water of bays and lagoons.

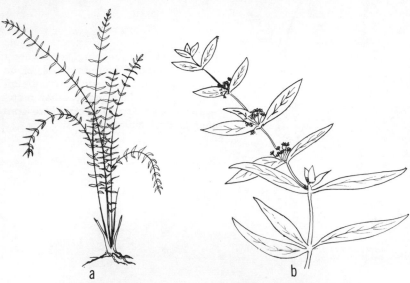

Fig. 24. *Decodon verticillatum* (Lythraceae) a. Plant (stylized);
b. Twig showing opposite leaves and whorls of flowers at the nodes.

28b. Stems semi-woody or herbaceous, but not spongy at the base; leaves opposite, sessile (Sea Milkwort). Fig. 25 . . . . *Glaux*

This is a perennial, semi-woody and profusely branched plant (when mature) which is confined to brackish tidal flats or to saline waters inland. It occurs on all coasts of continental United States. Flowers are solitary in the axils of linear or oval leaves and produce beaked capsules as fruits.

Fig. 25. *Glaux maritima*
(Primulaceae) a. Habit of
plant; b. Single flower.

24

29a. **(26) Leaves spirally arranged, arising from three sides of the stem** **30**

29b. **Leaves alternate or opposite**.............................**31**

30a. **Leaves broadly oval or orbicular in outline, coarsely serrate on the margin; bud scales several (Alder) Fig. 26**..........*Alnus*

There are several species of Alder which form thickets along lake shores and stream courses. The trees are monoecious, the flowers occurring in catkins. The pistillate persist as dry cones.

30b. **Leaves elongate and narrowly elliptic to nearly linear (rarely elongate-oval), usually with stipules (often deciduous); margins either finely or remotely serrate; bud scales 1; shrubs, marginal along stream courses and beaches (Willow). Fig. 27**.......*Salix*

There are numerous species of willow, given the ancient Celtic name "Salis" which means "near the water." Many are important as beach-builders and can be used in erosion control. The wood is used for making charcoal in some sections, and twigs are used in basket-making. Species are differentiated by morphological details of the flowers and leaves.

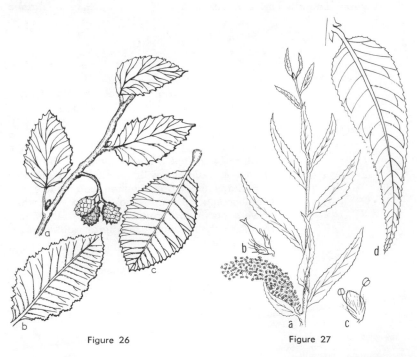

Figure 26   Figure 27

Fig. 26. *Alnus* (Betulaceae) a. Twig of *A. crispa* with carpellate flowers; b. *A. incana* leaf; c. *A. crispa* leaf.

Fig. 27. *Salix* (Salicaceae) a. Twig with staminate catkin; b. Scale with pistil; c. Scale with stamens; d. Leaf of *S. serissima*.

25

32a. Leaves lanceolate (or nearly linear), revolute (rolled under
along the margin), green above, decidedly whitened beneath
(Swamp Laurel). Fig. 27A..............................*Kalmia*

This is the Swamp Laurel or Bog Winter-
green growing characteristically in *Sphagnum*
bogs. They are low shrubs from 30 cm to nearly waist high. *Kalmia* is associated with *Ledum*
(Labrador Tea) and with *Chamaedaphne*
(Leather Leaf) and other members of the heath
family. *K. polifolia* with enrolled leaf margins
is perhaps the more common and widely distributed species. The showy pink or white
flowers occur in terminal racemes. In *K. angustifolia* the flowers are lateral, solitary or a
few together.

Fig. 27A. *Kalmia* (Eri-
caceae) a. *K. angustifolia*
twig showing opposite,
elliptical leaves and a
few saucer-shaped (pink
or white) flowers; b. *K.
polifolia* leaf showing enrolled margins.

32b. Leaves otherwise..33

33a. Leaves with several prominent veins, seen especially on the under side, curving boldly upward and outward from the midrib to the leaf margin which is slightly undulate, hairy on the under side; bark of stem red (Dogwood; Red Ozier Dogwood). Fig. 28..
....*Cornus stolonifera*

This is the common and widely distributed Red Ozier Dogwood. The shrub has umbels of small, white flowers which produce clusters of white berrylike fruits. This species is conspicuous about swamps, stream courses and lake shores in winter because of the showy red bark. Other *Cornus* species with gray or slightly red (purplish) bark (*C. Amomum*) may occur in the same habitat, the latter having pubescent twigs and leaves.

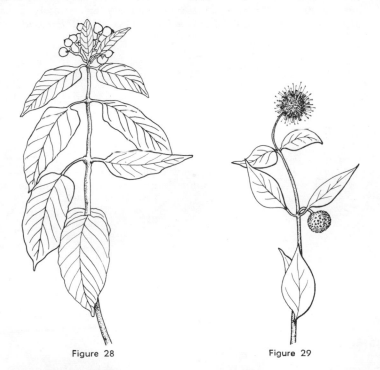

Figure 28   Figure 29

Fig. 28. *Cornus stolonifera* (Cornaceae) Twig showing terminal clump of berrylike fruits (white).

Fig. 29. *Cephalanthus occidentalis* (Rubiaceae) Twig with a terminal cluster of flowers and a mature, ball-like cluster of fruits.

33b. Lateral veins conspicuous but not so prominent on the lower surface, ending in a network at the margins which are entire; bark
not reddish; leaves rarely occurring in 3's as well as opposite
(Button Bush). Fig. 29........................... *Cephalanthus*
This is the only shrub in the United States (native) belonging to
the quinine family which is common in the tropics. The common name
is derived from the headlike cluster of pyramidate fruits terminal on
a long flower stalk. The shrubs occur marginally with Dogwood and
Willows.

34a. (31) Leaves broadly elliptic, with lateral veins very prominent
as seen from the under side, curving upward and outward to the
margins, not hairy on the underside; flowers small, in dense
custers; bark not reddish; shrubs of somewhat dry situations
but sometimes occurring with *Cornus stolonifera* near aquatic
habitats (Dogwood). Fig. 28...................... *Cornus* (p.p.)

34b. Leaves narrowly elliptic; without prominent veins showing on
the under side; shrubs of acid bogs(*)...................... 35

35a. Leaves with brownish scales above and below, showing as brown
dots on the upper surface; leaves coarsely or remotely serrate
along the apical margin (Leather Leaf). Fig. 30 .... *Chamaedaphne*

Chamaedaphne forms dense thickets in
Sphagnum bogs and in moist sandy soil.

Fig. 30. *Chamaedaphne
calyculata* (Ericaceae) a.
Twig showing leaf arrangement; b. Flower in axil of
leaf.

(*)See also *Ledum groenlandicum* (Laborador Tea), a shrub of bogs which has
alternate, narrow leaves that are densely brown-woolly on the under side; the capsule
elongate oval; also *Andromeda glaucophylla* (Bog Rosemary) that has revolute leaves
(rolled under along the margins) and with flattened or depressed globular fruits.

35b. Leaves pale or dark-green, without brownish scales, sometimes with dotlike glands or hairs, usually glabrous; leaf margins entire or finely serrate throughout (Blueberry; Cranberry). Fig. 23 . . . . *Vaccinium* (p.p.)

36a. (23) Leaves ribbonlike, grasslike, swordlike or linear, with parallel or subparallel margins, more than ten times the width in length; simple (but see *Podostemum*, Fig. 107); or plants having long, slender, naked stems (*Eleocharis*, Fig. 134, e.g.) with leaves reduced to sheaths at the base; bearing flowers and fruits at or near the apex (but see *Glaux*, Fig. 25) 232

36b. Leaves otherwise, not long ribbons nor grasslike and swordlike. .37

37a. Leaves with a broad blade of various shapes, not more than ten times the width in length; leaves simple or compound and sometimes divided into linear or threadlike segments, leaves with or without a petiole. 38

37b. Leaves in the form of small scales or leaflike joints, Fig. 4) green or colorless bracts or scales, sometimes underground on horizontal stems and occurring as forked linear threads (*Utricularia* spp. Fig. 116); in some plants leaves reduced to a rim at the stem nodes. 215

38a. Leaves in the form of hollow tubes or pitchers; insect-catching plants 39

38b. Leaves otherwise, variously shaped, elongate, spatulate, oval, elliptic or circular (at least in outline), or with sagittate blades; leaves with or without a petiole 40

39a. Leaves tubelike, pitcher-shaped, open or covered by a raised "awning" or a simple hood which has no downward projecting bracts (Pitcher Plant). Fig. 31 . . . . *Sarracenia*

Fig. 31. *Sarracenia purpurea* (Sarraceniaceae) Plant with a single flower.

This is the most common of the eastern pitcher plants. The liquid in the hollow leaf contains enzymes which digest the soft parts of insects captured. This is apparently the chief source of nitrogen in the plant's nutrition and metabolism. S. *Drummondi* occurs in southern bogs, has an awning or lid over the opening of the "pitcher." The procumbent leaves and the solitary flower of S. *purpurea*, borne on a naked scape are purplish, hence the species name. The southern U. S. species is known as Trumpets. Pitcher plants usually occur in *Sphagnum* bogs and in acid situations, but unexplainably S. *purpurea* is found in old bogs which have become basic, growing in sedge meadows.

39b. Leaves tubelike pitchers, hooded with an opening on its underside, bearing a persistent, forked, tonguelike bract (Pitcher Plant).
Fig. 32.................................*Darlingtonia californica*

This is the only species of western pitcher plant. The leaves appear in clusters,
straight and erect, with a hood over the
opening and with a forked, tonguelike
bract. Leaves vary in length from one or
two inches when young to 30 inches when
mature. The flowering scape is shorter
than the leaves and bears a single, nodding, purple and yellow blossom. The
species is confined to coastal *Sphagnum*
bogs of Oregon and northern California.

Fig. 32. *Darlingtonia californica* (Sarraceniaceae) Plant
with hooded leaves bearing
forked bracts.

40a. (38) Leaves with broad, floating blades, round oval or broadly
elliptic more than 2 cm wide, on long, slender petioles or stems
which arise from subterranean rootstocks, the petioles (when
stout) sometimes supporting blades in the air when water has
receded 41

40b. Leaves smaller, shaped and arranged otherwise.............46

41a. Leaves peltate..42

41b. Leaves not peltate, but with marginal petioles; blades deeply lobed basally **44**

42a. Floating blades linear-oblong, from a weakly erect, submersed stem that also bears opposite, finely dissected leaves (Fanwort, Parrot Feather). Fig. 33 .... *Cabomba*

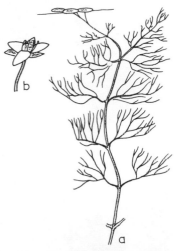

This species has both floating blades, oblong or obovate in shape, and highly dissected submersed leaves. The small waterlily flowers are white with yellow spots. *Cabomba* is useful as an aerator and is popular as a fish aquarium plant. Thus far the species is known from eastern and southern United States.

Fig. 33. *Cabomba caroliniana* (Nymphaeaceae) a. Portion of stem showing finely dissected submersed leaves and peltate floating leaves; b. Flower.

42b. Plants without finely dissected, submersed leaves **43**

43a. Leaves oval or elliptic, about 5 cm in long diameter, the petioles and stem thickly coated with a firm mucilage; flowers relatively small (lotuslike), sometimes opening under water (Water Shield). Fig. 34 . . . . *Brasenia*

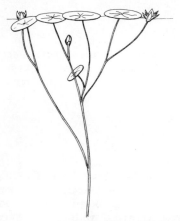

This species is widely distributed but somewhat uncommon. The plants grow in quiet water, often among emergent reeds and rushes. The firm, mucilaginous coating on the stem and petioles is so slippery that collecting by hand is difficult.

Fig. 34. *Brasenia Schreberi* (Nymphaeaceae) Portion of plant showing leaves with peltate, floating blades.

43b. Leaves much larger, 3 dm or more across, blades often held above the water surface by a stout petiole; flowers light yellow, large, showy, lotuslike blooms (Lotus). Fig. 35 . . . . *Nelumbo*

The American Lotus occurs mostly throughout the Ohio and lower Mississippi valleys, although in favorable situations it grows in upper Midwest and New England states. The lotus forms dense meadows in lakes and lagoons, with the peltate leaves usually raised above the water surface on stout petioles. The disclike receptacle has "pepper-box" sockets in which nutlike fruits develop. These are known as Chinquapins and are collected for food by both Man and animals. A tribe of Indians in the South were known as the Chinquapin Eaters. The rhizome is also used as food by muskrats.

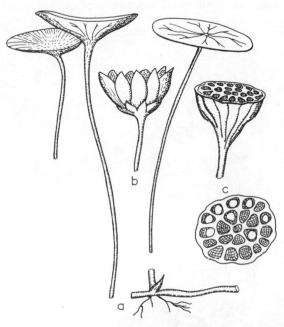

Fig. 35. *Nelumbo lutea* (Nymphaeaceae) a. Rhizome and portions of emergent, peltate leaves; b. Lotus type of blossom; c. Receptacle with nutlike fruits (Chinquapins).

44a. (41) Leaves with orbicular or cordate blades, with crenate margins, floating at the surface on long, slender petioles arising from either a slender, erect stem, or from a horizontal rhizome, veins branching and then recurved to unite with one another; the upright stem giving rise to aquatic roots at the base of the leaf

petiole; flowers solitary or several together arising from the erect stem, the corolla rotate, 5-parted (Floating Heart). Fig. 36 . . . .
. . . . *Nymphoides*

The deeply lobed blades have a palmate venation and float at the surface on long petioles which are clustered at the end of horizontal rhizomes. The rhizomes usually have runners. Flower stalks and adventitious roots develop from the upper section of the petioles. There are several species, all known from eastern and southern United States. *Nymphoides* is a useful aquarium plant.

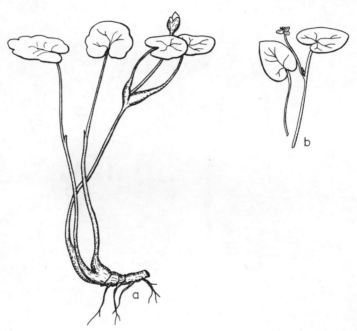

Fig. 36. *Nymphoides* (Menyanthaceae) a. *Nymphoides peltatum;*
b. Leaves and flower of *N. cordatum.*

44b. Plants otherwise 45

45a. Leaves broadly oval (up to 2 times the width in length), or nearly round, with broadly rounded basal lobes which (often) overlap, the margins entire; flowers yellow, tuliplike; fruit a swollen, flat-topped urn with a broad stigmatic surface (Yellow Water Lily). Fig. 37 . . . . *Nuphar*

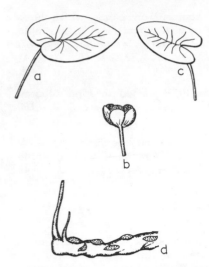

Fig. 37. *Nuphar* (Nymphaeaceae) a,b. Leaf and flower of *N. advena;* c. Leaf of *N. variegatum;* d. Rhizome.

This genus has yellow, tuliplike flowers and broadly oval, bilobed leaf blades on long petioles that grow from thick, subterranean rhizomes. Petioles may be as much as 12 feet long. Young, submersed leaves are often red-tinged. The lobes of the leaf often overlap, especially in *N. advena.* This is perhaps the most widely distributed species; others are somewhat local in several sections of the United States. Many birds and animals make use of the flowers, seeds, leaves and rhizomes, the latter being the chief source of food for muskrats. Deer and moose browse on the leaves, as do insects.

45b. Leaves nearly round in outline, with lobes which have a prominent recurved apiculation; flowers white (or violet; cultivated species variously colored), lotuslike; fruit a globular, fleshy body with a narrow, median, stigmatic surface (Water Lily). Fig. 38. . . . .*Nymphaea*

Fig. 38. *Nymphaea* (Nymphaeaceae) Leaves and blossom.

This genus has relatively large, showy, lotuslike blooms, white or violet. The leaf blades are nearly circular but are deeply lobed. At the base of each lobe is a recurved apiculation. One common species, *N. odorata* is purple on the underside of the leaves and has purple stripes on the petioles, *N. tetragona* has flowers one-fourth the size of the more common *N. odorata* and *N. tuberosa. N. tetragona* has a curious disjunct distribution throughout the United States, occurring in the northeast and northwest sections, with one station known from the Great Lakes region. *Nymphaea* occurs along with *Nuphar* but may be more common by itself in soft or acid-water habitats.

52a. Leaves with deltoid blades on long petioles which are inflated, alternate but forming a whorled rosette at the surface (Water Chestnut). Fig. 39 . . . .*Trapa*

The stem of this plant is long and lax; bears deltoid leaves which have an inflated petiole. In the lower part of the stem are numerous, finely branched adventitious roots which increase gas absorption. The subterranean roots show a negative phototropism and emerge into the water, further increasing the gas-absorbing surfaces. The solitary flowers have a two- chambered ovary in which large, triangular seeds are produced. The fleshy seed (Water Chestnut) is used for food, especially in Chinese dishes. This species, introduced from Asia, is known from eastern and northeastern United States, especially in habitats with organic mud bottoms.

Fig. 39. *Trapa natans* (Onagraceae) a. Habit of plant with upper leaves forming a rosette, lateral leaves with inflated petiole, highly branched adventitious roots; b. fruit.

52b. Leaves shaped otherwise 53

53a. Leaves narrowly elliptic to ovoid, 3 (rarely more) at each node (rarely 2 opposite leaves); plants dioecious; pistillate flowers floating at the surface on threadlike stalks, petals 3, white or pink (Waterweed). Fig. 40 . . . .*Elodea*

Anacharis is a synonym for this genus known commonly as Water Weed. The stems are bushy with whorls of ovate leaves. The plants reproduce actively by fragmentation and although they develop as rooted stems they frequently become free-floating. The two most common and dioecious species in this country are *E. canadensis* and *E. occidentale*. The latter has slender, nearly linear leaves, the former ovate, either lax or sometimes rigid.

Elodea densa, introduced from Brazil, is an escape and forms profuse, often troublesome growths especially in Pacific coast states. All species are popular as aquarium plants because they are efficient oxygenators. Carpellate flowers are white or pink, borne on long

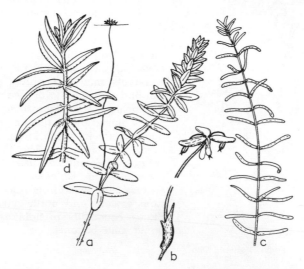

Fig. 40. *Elodea* (Hydrocharitaceae) a. Portion of stem of *E. canadensis* with a pistillate flower; b. Basal spathe and a floating pistillate flower; c. *Elodea occidentale*, section of stem; d. *Elodea densa*.

threadlike peduncles that arise from a basal spathe. These float at the surface in such a way as to expose the curved styles and stigmatic surfaces. The staminate flowers occur in a basal spathe, are released so that they float about on the surface where they come in contact with the carpellate flowers.

53b. Leaves narrowly linear, many at each node (rarely with some leaves alternate on the same stem also) (Water Mare's Tail). Fig. 41 ....*Hippuris*

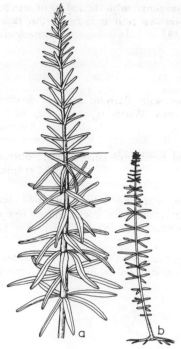

These plants are limp and flexible when submersed, with whorls of lax leaves, but are erect and rigid, with short leaves when emergent. It is highly useful as an oxygenator. The species is widely distributed throughout the United States and occurs as one of the few aquatic plants in arctic pools and lakes.

Fig. 41. *Hippuris vulgaris* (Haloragidaceae) a. Habit of plant with submersed and emergent stem and leaves; b. Habit of marginal plant with somewhat rigid leaves.

55a. Leaves deeply lobed (simple but nearly compound), 3 at a node (although usually opposite) teeth bluntly pointed; flowers green, solitary in the axils of leaves. Fig. 42..... *Leucospora (Conobea)*

This is the only species in the genus; grows on shores or in lake marginal water. It is found mostly in midwestern United States, but occurs southward. The leaves are either opposite or whorled and are deeply pinnate-lobed. The greenish flowers are borne singly (usually) in the axils of leaves. There is no known biological importance.

55b. Leaves simple, linear or oblong, entire margins, several (usually 4) in a whorl at each node; flowers small (2-3 mm wide), white, stalked, in a cyme borne in the axils of leaf whorls; stems 4-angled (Bedstraw). Fig. 43.................................... *Galium*

In this genus there are whorls of linear leaves and panicles of small, white flowers (or sometimes only one, or two). Submersed species are not beset with hooklike spines as are the terrestrial ones. *G. trifidum* has thin, hooked, flower stalks whereas in *G. tinctorium* they are thicker and straight.

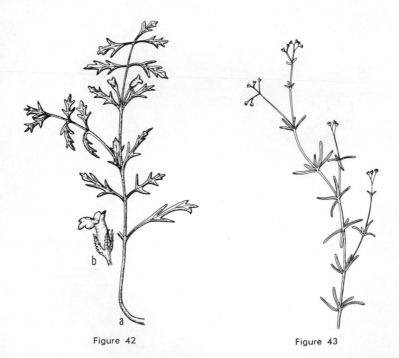

Figure 42   Figure 43

Fig. 42. *Leucospora multifida (Conobea)* (Scrophulariaceae) a. Habit of plant with opposite, deeply incised leaves; b. Single flower.

Fig. 43. *Galium* (Rubiaceae) a. Portion of branch of *Galium tinctorium.*

56a. (54) Erect stems with many elongate and linear leaves (6-12) at each node (a bottle-brush type of growth); upper leaves short and somewhat rigid (2-3 mm wide), lower leaves (especially if submersed) long and lax, collapsing when removed from the water (Water Mare's Tail). Fig. 41.....................*Hippuris*

56b. Erect stem with leaves shaped and arranged otherwise......57

57a. Short herbs, about ½ M, with rounded, oval or mostly lanceolate leaves, opposite or alternate (See 58b), but sometimes whorled; leaves gland-dotted and often with a fringe along the basal margin of the very short petiole; base of leaf tapering; flowers yellow (often purple-spotted), either solitary in the axils of leaves or in a terminal raceme, capsule of flower globular; ovary and capsule 1-celled (Loosestrife). Fig. 44.........................*Lysimachia*

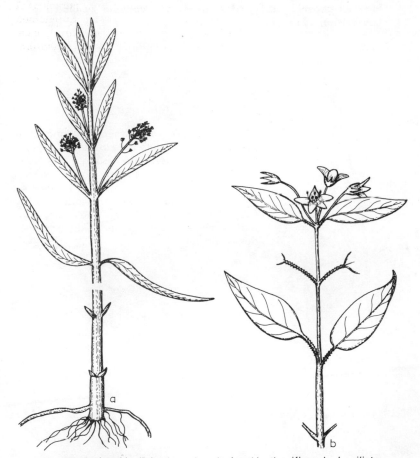

Fig. 44. *Lysimachia* (Primulaceae) a. *Lysimachia thyrsiflora;* b. *L. ciliata.*

41

This genus shows considerable variation in leaf arrangement, but usually they have glandular dots and most species have ciliate fringes along the basal margins of the blade as well as along the petioles. The latter character varies in different parts of the United States. *L. terrestris* with square stems and *L. thyrsiflora* with round stems are the most common species. The latter occurs both in the water (emergent) and along lake shores, in wet meadows, etc.

57b. **Tall, often rank herbs, as much as 2 M high; leaves ovate to linear-lanceolate, and sessile, sometimes whorled but mostly opposite (see 58b), usually somewhat heart-shaped or lobed at the base which is not fringed along the margins, sessile on usually somewhat angular stems; flowers purple (or white), in long terminal spikes (or in some species solitary in the axils of leaves); capsule subcylindric; ovary and capsule 2-celled (Spiked Loosestrife). Fig. 45** .... *Lythrum*

This is a tall, rank weed, growing along shores and in wet meadows. The purple flowers are in terminal spikes. The leaves are sessile, with a slightly lobed base. *L. salicaria* and *L. alatum* are two species distributed throughout eastern and southern United States. The former has the upper leaves shorter and partly hidden by the dense flowers.

Fig. 45. *Lythrum* (Lythraceae) a. Portion of *Lythrum Salicaria*; b. Flower.

59a. Plants floating; leaves opposite...........................60

59b. Plants anchored by roots, in the water or on shore; leaves opposite
....61

60a. Plant consisting of a pair of opposite, leaflike segments or joints,
about 5 to 8 mm wide, the under side purple and bearing several
rootlets from each joint (Great Duckweed). Fig. 3........*Spirodela*

60b. Plant a short, floating stem with 2 or 3 pairs of opposite, circular
leaves, 1 cm or less across, bearing stiff bristles on the upper
surface; no roots but highly divided ventral leaves (Floating Fern).
Fig. 20 ....*Salvinia*

61a. Leaves with entire margins................................62

61b. Leaves with teeth, serrations, or crenulate, or margin lobed and
incised 89

62a. Plants submersed and essentially rooted to the bottom, sometimes
at 8 M (often becoming free-floating); with or without floating leaves..63

62b. Plants rooted on shore or in shallow water, emergent, sprawling
or growing erect at margins of aquatic habitats..............70

63a. Plants with variously shaped leaves: linear lanceolate, elliptic
or ribbonlike, sometimes with oval floating leaves; leaves mostly
alternate (See 105a), but rarely opposite, with a stipule at the
base of the leaf, free or forming a sheath about the stem just
above the leaf attachment (Pondweed). Fig. 46.....*Potamogeton*
This is the Pondweed genus, with about 45 species distributed in
the United States. The leaves are variable in shape; broad blades,
ribbons, or narrowly linear. Some have both narrow, submersed leaves
and broad, floating (oval or elliptic) blades. The alternate leaves with

a stipule, and the morphology of the flowers and fruits are characteristic features which separate this genus from other aquatics. The flowers have a perianth composed of a 4-lobed calyx, 4 stamens and usually 4 carpels, each of which forms a one-seeded drupe. Many species are highly important for bird and animal food, in oxygenation of water, and because of the substantial amount of organic matter they produce in the aquatic environment.

Fig. 46. *Potamogeton* (Naidaceae) a. *Potamogeton natans;* b. *P. Richardsonii;* c. *P. gramineus;* d. *Potamogeton* flower, side view (diagrammatic); e. Flower, vertical view (diagrammatic); f. *P. natans* fruit; g. *P. pectinatus;* h. *P. pectinatus,* leaf and stipule; i. *P. pectinatus,* fruits; j. *P. Robbinsii;* k. *P. amplifolius;* l. *P. zosteriformis.*

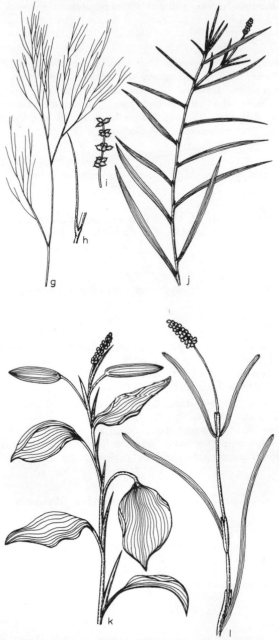

Fig. 46. Continued.

63b. Plants having leaves without stipules; leaves shaped differently.
. 64

64a. Stem bushy with opposite (but mostly whorled), elliptic or oval,
sessile leaves, arranged along the entire length; small white (5-8
mm) carpellate flowers floating at the surface on long, white
threads from the submersed stem; staminate flowers with 3
sepals and petals, bearing 3-9 anthers, borne sessile in the axils
of leaves and submersed (Waterweed). Fig. 40 . . . . *Elodea*

64b. Stems with leaves shaped and arranged otherwise 65

65a. Plants with a pair of oval, floating leaf blades and highly dissected, submersed leaves (Fanwort, Parrot Feather). Fig. 33 . . . . .
. . . .*Cabomba*

65b. Plants with leaves shaped and arranged otherwise 66

66a. Plants with slender, mostly vertical, threadlike stems bearing
narrow, elongate or spatula-shaped opposite leaves which are
crowded and form a rosette at the surface (at least when fully
developed); flower solitary, sessile in axils of leaves; fruit bilobed,
nutlike (Water Starwort). Fig. 47 . . . .*Callitriche*
This genus is characterized by the slender, threadlike submersed
stems which often do not reach the surface. Leaves are linear to
spatula-shaped on the same plant and they may become crowded
and form a rosette at the water surface, hence the name Water Starwort. The tender plants are used by diving birds for food.

66b. Plants with leaves shaped and arranged otherwise 67

67a. Plants growing erect or essentially so, or lax, especially in submersed species, with oval, elliptic to lanceolate leaves which
are sessile; leaves with translucent dots when emergent (Goat
Weed; St. John's-wort). Fig. 48 . . . .*Hypericum*(*)

_____

(*)*Hypericum virginicum* with showy pink-purple flowers is found often in bogs
and swamps. The name is synonymous with *Triadenum virginicum*.

Several species of the genus grow either submersed or emergent, and on lake shores, wet meadows, etc. The leaves are oval or lanceolate, sessile and usually have transparent spots in the blades, especially when leaves are above water. In most species the flowers are yellow, in both terminal and axilary racemes or corymbs. Several species are known to be used for food by birds and browsing animals.

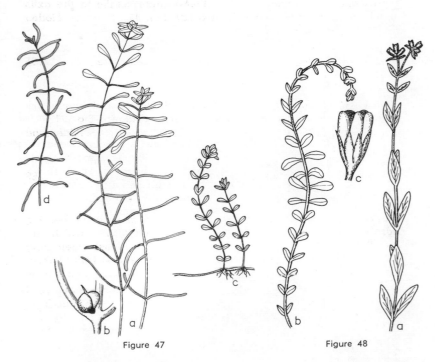

Figure 47   Figure 48

Fig. 47. *Callitriche* (Callitrichaceae) a. *Callitriche palustris,* habit; b. fruit; c. *C. deflexa* habit; d. *C. hermaphroditica* habit.

Fig. 48. *Hypericum* (Hypericaceae) a. *Hypericum boreale;* b. *H. ellipticum;* c. *H. punctatum* flower.

67b. Plants otherwise, creeping, sometimes with erect shoots **68**

68a. **Leaves linear or in some species oblong-lanceolate with entire margins; plants with creeping rootstocks from which erect or sprawling shoots arise, forming extensive floating mats, especially in shallow water; flowers 5-parted, in heads which are either axial and sessile or on long shoots, either terminal on the stem or in the axils of leaves; (plants also marginal, growing on mud flats) (Alligator Weed). Fig. 49** . . . .*Alternanthera*

This species is known from the Gulf region of the United States. It is a low, sprawling weed with narrowly elliptic, opposite leaves and with heads of small flowers on a long peduncle. Plants grow abundantly in ponds and slowly flowing streams.

Fig. 49. *Alternanthera philoxeroides* (Amaranthaceae) a. Habit of plant portion; b. Single flower.

68b. **Plants otherwise; leaves shaped differently** 69

69a. **Leaves broadly oval to nearly round, sessile and somewhat clasping the stem; plants greenish; flowers in 2's and 3's in the axils of leaves; leaves palmately veined (Water Hyssop). Fig. 50** . . . . .
. . . . *Bacopa* (*Hydrotrida*)

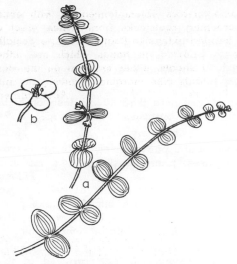

In this genus plants are sprawling or creeping and bushy. The small, yellow, two-lipped flowers are solitary in the axils of leaves. The common species is *Bacopa Monnieria*, a plant of shores and of brackish ponds on the Atlantic and Gulf coasts.

Fig. 50. *Bacopa (Bramia)* (Scrophulariaceae) a. Branches with nearly circular leaves and axial flowers; b. Single flower.

69b. Leaves elliptic or oval, mostly tapering at the base and usually with a petiole (sessile, but with a narrowed base in some species), 1-4 cm long; leaves pinnately veined (False Loosestrife). Fig. 51
. . . .*Ludwigia*

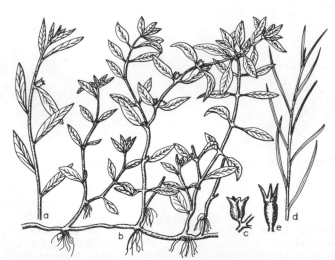

Fig. 51. *Ludwigia* (Onagraceae) a. *Ludwigia polycarpa*; b. *L. palustris*; c. Calyx; d. *L. linearis*; e. Fruit.

49

There are many species of *Ludwigia*, erect and terrestrial, or prostrate and creeping on shores, or submersed. The common aquatic species is *L. palustris*, a somewhat fleshy herb with opposite leaves and with unlike, sessile flowers in the axils. Stems and leaves are reddish. It is a species widely distributed over the United States. Plants are used by muskrats for food.

70a. **(62) Plants of dwarf stature, no more than 10 cm long or high, mostly creeping, with some erect branches**....................**71**

70b. **Plants larger, erect in part or completely so**.................**72**

71a. **Plants 6-8 cm high, with succulent, puffy, somewhat linear leaves which are joined at their bases; plants mostly of tidal marshes (Pigmy Weed). Fig. 52**....................................*Tillaea*

This is a small, tufted and sprawling weed with opposite, linear and succulent leaves. It is found in brackish situations along all coasts, but apparently is known from only a few locations. It is the only member of the Crassulaceae which is aquatic or semi-aquatic.

71b. **Plants up to 10 cm long or high; leaves narrowly oval to nearly linear, somewhat spatulate in some species, narrowed at the base and not adjoined; plants of muddy bottoms or in tidal flats, prostrate and sometimes matted (Waterwort). Fig. 53**.....*Elatine*

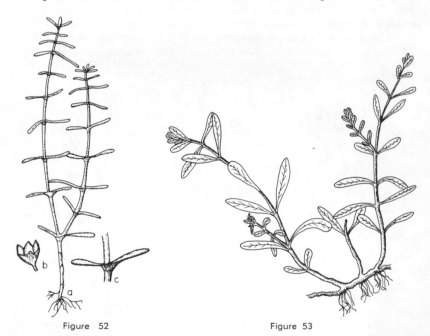

Figure 52   Figure 53

Fig. 52. *Tillaea aquatica* (Crassulaceae) a. Habit; b. Single flower; c. Opposite leaves joined at the base.

Fig. 53. *Elatine triandra* (Elatinaceae) Habit of plant.

There are many species of this genus which are aquatic or semi-aquatic, the most widely distributed being *E. americana* which can be found in tidal marshes and on shores of ponds throughout the United States. The leaves vary from oval to oblanceolate; are glabrous and somewhat fleshy. It is thought that some species are used by ducks.

72a. (70) Leaves elongate, linear (oblong), approaching lanceolate in
some 73

72b. Leaves other shaped, mostly lanceolate or oblong lanceolate...77

73a. Leaves with transparent or translucent dots (except that they may not show in submersed leaves), seen by holding leaf to the light and examining with a hand lens (Goat Weed; St. John's-wort). Fig. 48................................*Hypericum*

73b. Leaves without translucent dots...........................74

74a. Plants with hard or semi-woody stems, especially at the base; leaves bluntly pointed; flowers solitary in leaf axils; calyx cylindrical and striated (Spiked Loosestrife). Fig. 45.................
....*Lythrum* (*L. lineare*)

74b. Plants not tough and semi-woody at the stem base..........75

75a. Leaves sharply pointed at the apex and long-tapering, about 12 mm wide; prominent lateral veins from a conspicuous midrib; flowers in sessile or stalked heads (Alligator Weed). Fig. 49....
....*Alternanthera*

75b. Leaves smaller, 1.5 to 6 mm wide, shaped differently; flowers arranged otherwise.......................................76

76a. Leaves blunt-pointed or very briefly tapering; sessile, mostly oblong or eliptic but sometimes approaching linear; calyx bell-shaped with deep, rounded lobes; plants of coastal regions or salt marshes (Sea Milkwort). Fig. 25..........................*Glaux*

76b. Leaves blunt-pointed or rounded at the apex, not sessile but with short petioles, oblanceolate to spatulate; calyx urn-shaped with short-pointed lobes (Tooth-cup). Fig. 54..............*Rotala*

Plants have erect stems which may be as much as 50 cm tall with opposite, elliptical, oval or oblanceolate leaves. The solitary flowers in the leaf axils produce urnlike, 4-valved capsules. Plants inhabit shores and wet meadows. *R. ramosior* is know from rice fields.

77a. (72) Leaves lanceolate or oblong lanceolate (See Fig. 45)......78

77b. Leaves other shapes.......................................81

78a. Plants erect with elongate-lanceolate, acutely pointed leaves that are dotted with dark glands; flowers yellow, in dense terminal or axial racemes, in some species the stems angular because of ridges (Loosestrife). Fig. 44......... *Lysimachia* (*L. thyrsiflora*)

78b. Leaves without dark glands; flowers arranged otherwise 79

79a. Erect shoots from creeping rootstocks; flowers in heads or short spikes on long peduncles..................................80

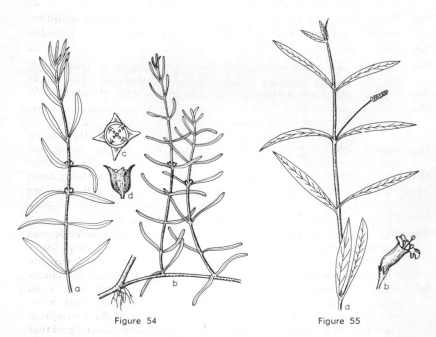

Figure 54   Figure 55

Fig. 54. *Rotala* (Lythraceae) a. *Rotala ramosior*; b. *R. diandra*; c., d. Flower in vertical and lateral views.

Fig. 55. *Dianthera* (*Justicia*) *americana* (Acanthaceae) a. Section of stem and one axial inflorescence; b. Single flower.

79b. Plants without creeping rootstocks, erect with a semi-woody base; flowers solitary or in whorls in the axils of leaves, forming a terminal spike (Spiked Loosestrife). Fig. 45.............*Lythrum*

80a. Flowers purple, the corolla irregular with the upper lip notched, the lower 3-lobed; stamens 2; leaves willowlike, rather rigid and straight, directed upward to 15 cm long; stems up to 10 dm high (Water Willow). Fig. 55.............................*Dianthera*
This species occurs throughout eastern and midwestern states. The opposite, elongate-elliptic leaves are similar to those of a willow. The small, purple flowers are in heads on long peduncles. *D. ovata* occurs mostly in southern states. The seeds of *Dianthera* are eaten by grouse.

80b. Flowers greenish or white, with a perianth of 5 sepals unequal in length; leaves oblong-lanceolate, but often nearly linear, not rigid, curved and somewhat drooping (Alligator Weed). Fig. 49..
....*Alternanthera*

81a. (77) Leaves elliptical or elongate-elliptic (sometimes nearly lanceolate) 82

81b. Leaves broadly oval to nearly round (some species with linear or elongate leaves also on the same stem)..................87

82a. Plants with semi-woody, perennial bases giving rise to whiplike, annual branches (Swamp Loosestrife). Fig. 24...........*Decodon*

82b. Plants otherwise...83

83a. Flowers and fruits borne in terminal racemes or in clusters, or one or two on stalks in the axils of upper leaves.............84

83b. Flowers and fruits solitary and sessile in the axils of leaves...85

84a. Leaves, especially when emergent, showing translucent dots when held to the light (Goat Weed; St. John's-wort). Fig. 48.....
....*Hypericum*

84b. Leaves without translucent dots; often with fringes along the lower margins of leaves (Loosestrife). Fig. 44.......*Lysimachia*

85a. (83) Plants dwarf, 4-5 cm long; prostrate on shores, portions erect when submersed, but very limp; fruit a thin-walled pod, showing the seeds; leaves 1 cm long or less (Waterwort). Fig. 53...*Elatine*

85b. Plants larger, with different type of fruit....................86

86a. Plants with ascending stems from a slender rootstock; leaves usually opposite below, alternate above; perianth of 5 calyx lobes (no petals), and whitish; ovary superior; fruit a beaked capsule with the style persisting (Sea Milkwort). Fig. 25...........*Glaux*

86b. Plants prostrate on and rooting in mud, with roots from stem nodes, or floating on the water; (some species erect, and if so, with linear-lanceolate leaves); leaves mostly opposite throughout the stem (in some species broadly oval to nearly round); perianth of 4, usually reddish sepals; ovary inferior; fruit a capsule, broader than long or enlarged above the middle (False Loosestrife). Fig. 51...*Ludwigia*

87a. (81) Leaves, especially when emergent, with translucent spots, easily seen with a hand lens when the leaf is held to the light (Goat Weed; St. John's-wort). Fig. 48.................*Hypericum*

87b. Leaves without translucent spots...........................88

88a. Sprawling and creeping plants (or with floating stems); flowers stalked, solitary in the axils of leaves (Water Hyssop). Fig. 50...
....*Bacopa*

88b. Plants erect; stems not woody, but hard and stiff; flowers purple (Spiked Loosestrife). Fig. 45...........................*Lythrum*

89a. (61) Leaves crenulate, sometimes with sharp crenulations approaching serrations (See Fig. 42); sometimes crenulations deep, so as to form lobes which have entire margins...............90

89b. Leaves with serrate margins (sometimes with coarse serrations, so deep as to give a nearly lobed condition as in *Lycopus americanus*, e.g.)...95

This is the only species of *Potamogeton* which does not have entire leaf margins. It is generally distributed throughout the United States wherever there are suitable habitats.

Fig. 56. *Potamogeton crispus* (Naiadaceae) a. Habit of plant portion, b. Single leaf showing crinkly, finely serrate margin.

90a. Plants with stipules at the base of the leaves (usually leaves alternate, but rarely opposite or nearly so); leaf margins with numerous, minute crenulations (Pondweed). Fig. 56.............
....*Potamogeton crispus*

90b. Plants without stipules.....................................91

91a. Leaves deeply lobed, pinnately divided and nearly compound. Fig. 42...*Leucospora*

91b. Leaves not lobed, crenulations sometimes few and nearly lacking.
....92

92a. Flowers numerous, relatively small, in racemes in the axils of leaves (terminal racemes also) which are sessile and in some species clasping the stem, up to 20 mm wide (Speedwell). Fig. 57
....*Veronica* (p.p.)

Fig. 57. *Veronica* (Scrophulariaceae) a. *Veronica americana* habit; b. Single flower; c. Leaves.

There are several species which are semi-aquatic, the most common being *V. americana*. The elliptic or lanceolate leaves are coarsely serrate. The blue and white corollas are irregular, the flowers arranged in terminal or axial racemes. Except that beds of plants serve as good soil binders there is no known biological importance.

92b. Flowers solitary (or 2, 3) in the axils of leaves..............93

93a. Leaf margins conspicuously crenulate (sometimes somewhat serrate); flowers showy, distinctly bilobed or 2-lipped, yellow, rose or blue (Monkey Flower). Fig. 58 . . . . *Mimulus*

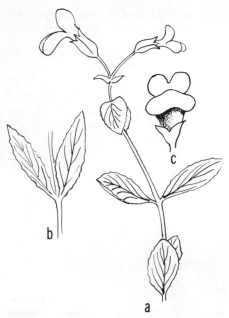

This genus includes several species that inhabit pond and stream margins, or occur in springs where they often become rank and sprawling. The flowers are usually yellow, but *M. Lewisii* is bright pink to rose-colored and *M. ringens* is blue. *M. moschatus* is a low, creeping species bearing sticky hairs; appears woolly.

Fig. 58. *Mimulus* (Scrophulariaceae) a. *Mimulas guttatus;* b. *M. alatus* leaves; c. Flower, *M. guttatus.*

93b. Leaf margins with few crenulations (or none); flowers nearly regular or weakly bilobed, sometimes campanulate 94

94a. Plants low and creeping, often rooting at the nodes (frequently floating); flowers with 4 stamens, all with anthers (Water Hyssop). Fig. 50 . . . . *Bacopa*

94b. Plants erect, to 3 cm high; flowers with 4 stamens, only 2 with anthers (False Pimpernel). Fig. 59 . . . . *Lindernia*

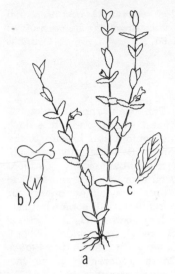

This species and *L. anagallidea* are the most common species, growing along stream and pond margins. The opposite leaves (15 mm long) are ovate in the latter species, become distinctly smaller toward the upper section of the stem. The purple flowers are on slender, axial stalks.

Fig. 59. *Lindernia dubia* (Scrophulariaceae) a. Habit; b. Flower; c. Leaf.

97a. **Plants with relatively small, succulent leaves (6 mm to 2 cm long, rarely as much as 4 cm) with wax droplets; stems hollow; flowers tubular (Hedge Hyssop). Fig. 60..................*Gratiola***

The somewhat tubular, 2-lipped, yellow and white flowers contain stiff bristles in the throat. Some species are submersed but mostly *Gratiola* occurs on muddy shores. The plants are either annual or perennial, with somewhat succulent leaves. *G. neglecta* is common and widely distributed over the United States. There apparently is no biological importance.

Fig. 60. *Gratiola* (Scrophulariaceae) a. *Gratiolo virginiana;* b. *G. lutea* flower.

97b. **Plants with thin leaves and mostly larger than above; stems not hollow (but some growth forms of *Mimulus* may be hollow)....98**

98a. **Plants creeping, often rooting at the nodes; leaves often nearly entire, with few serrations................................100**

98b. **Plants erect; serrations conspicuous........................99**

99a. Flowers tubular-campanulate, 2-lipped, with the upper lip strongly arched; flowers blue (Skullcap). Fig. 61............*Scutellaria*

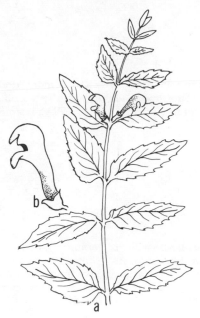

This is the most common species in aquatic situations. It has showy, purple, tubular flowers which have an arched corolla. The plants grow in marshes and wet meadows and swales. The leaves are sessile, whereas in S. *laterifolia* they are petiolate with flowering shoots axial. Typical of the family, the stems are 4-angled.

Fig. 61. *Scutellaria epilobifolia* (Labiatae) a. Habit; 2. Flower.

99b. Flowers mostly funnelform, bilobed, the upper lobe composed of one petal spreading from the funnel, the lower lip composed of 4 petals, the corolla (yellow, blue or rose) forming the familiar "monkey face" (Monkey Flower). Fig. 58.........*Mimulus* (p.p.)

100a. (98) Stems and leaves fleshy; leaves sometimes entire rather than serrate, broadly oval to nearly round; corolla extended but slightly beyond the calyx; petals white with the tube yellow (Water Hyssop). Fig. 50............ *Bacopa* (*Hydrotrida, Macuillamia*)

100b. Stems and leaves not fleshy but the stem often succulent and hollow; corolla yellow, rose or purple, the throat spotted (Monkey Flower). Fig. 58...............................*Mimulus* (p.p.)

101a. (96) Flowers in spikes, occurring in pairs which are more and more closely arranged toward the apex; leaves usually elliptic or lanceolate (False Dragonhead). Fig. 62..........*Physostegia*

This is a tall herb with a terminal spike of showy purple or blue flowers (sometimes white). Plants inhabit weedy or grassy lake margins and swales. *P. virginiana* is perhaps the most common species and attains a height of 1½ M.

Fig. 62. *Physostegia virginiana* (Labiatae) a. Anterior section of flowering stem; b. Single flower.

101b. Flowers arranged otherwise...............................102

102a. Flowers arranged on a flat receptacle and usually of two forms, central ones tubular, the marginal flowers forming petal-like rays (sunflower or daisy type); emergent leaves elliptic with serrate margins; submersed leaves finely dissected (Water Marigold). Fig. 63 . . . . *Megalodonta*

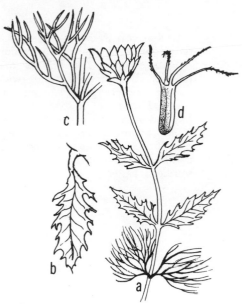

Until these submersed plants become emergent and develop their elliptical, serrate leaves, they may be confused with some species of *Ranunculus* or *Neobeckia*. The submersed leaves are finely divided dichotomously. The plants grow in relatively shallow water with silted bottoms *M. Beckii*, sometimes named *Bidens Beckii*, is common in northeast and northwest United States. The "daisy" type of bloom is large and conspicuous, appears above the surface of the water.

Fig. 63. *Megalodonta Beckii* (Compositae) a. Upper portion of stem showing two forms of leaves; b. Emergent leaf; c. Submersed leaf; d. Achene.

102b. Flowers arranged in other types of heads, or in spikelike racemes 103

103a. Flowers closely arranged in oval or conical heads, borne on relatively long peduncles from the leaf axils; leaves with rough white hairs on the underside (Frog-fruit). Fig. 64 . . . . *Lippia*

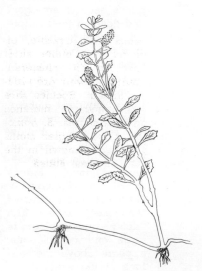

Except for *Verbena* this is the only genus of the family which is semi-aquatic. The flowers are tubular, but almost rotate, with corolla slightly 2-lipped, pink or white. Plants are low and creeping and form mats on moist shores. *L. lanceolata* is the most widely distributed species whereas *L. nodiflora* seems to be confined to southern states.

Fig. 64. *Lippia nodiflora* (Verbenaceae) Habit of plant.

103b. Flowers in clusters, appearing sessile in the axils of leaves . . 104

104a. Flowers decidedly 2-lipped, relatively large (1 cm or more long); lobes of the corolla equalling the tube in length; leaves oblong-lanceolate to elliptic (Hedge Nettle). Fig. 65 . . . . *Stachys*

This genus has opposite, elliptical blades with either short or long petioles. The clustered, whorled, purple flowers are tubular and 2-lipped. Species are widely distributed in marshes and along lake shores. *S. homotricha* with hairy, 4-angled stems and leaves is well-known in the eastern and midwest states.

Fig. 65. *Stachys tenuifolia* (Labiatae)
a. Upper portion of stem; b. Flower.

104b. Flowers relatively small, not strongly 2-lipped but almost regular
. . . . 105

105a. Plants aromatic (mint odor); leaves ovate to elliptic with serrations that are mostly fine, 9 to 13 or more on a side (Mint). Fig. 66 . . . .*Mentha*

The species of this genus are quickly identified by their mint odor. Several are marginal or grow in moist meadows. *M. arvensis* with its dense whorls of sessile flowers is probably the most common and widely distributed. *M. spicata* with flowers in terminal spikes and without leaves in the inflorescence is spearmint. *M. piperata* with relatively large leaves is the common peppermint.

Fig. 66. *Mentha piperata* (Labiatae) a. Upper portion of plant; b. Flower.

105b. Plants not aromatic; leaves oval or broadly elliptic with mostly coarse and relatively few serrations (5 to 7 on a side) (Water Horehound). Fig. 67 . . . .*Lycopus*

Species of this genus are mostly un-branched; have opposite, serrate or deep-ly lobed leaves. The flowers are in dense whorls somewhat similar to *Mentha* and other members of the family. The stem is square and often hairy. *L. americana* is probably the best-known and widely distributed, a species that is nearly glab-rous. Plants are marginal or emergent in shallow water.

Fig. 67. *Lycopus americana* (Labiatae) a. Anterior portion of stem; b. Single flower.

106a. (58) Leaves alternate or in whorls of three................107

106b. Leaves basal, or in a rosette...........................152

107a. Plants floating, consisting of a short stem bearing pairs of broad, rounded, dorsal leaves and finely dissected submersed, ventral leaves, arranged in whorls; dorsal leaves ½ to 1 cm wide, bearing erect bristles on the upper epidermis (Water Fern; Floating Moss). Fig. 20........................*Salvinia*

107b. Leaves shaped and arranged otherwise; plants attached or only incidentally afloat...108

108a. Leaves lobed, sometimes deeply incised or pinnately compound 109

108b. Leaves not lobed, margins serrate or entire..............122

109a. Leaves broadly rounded, heart-shaped, or oval, mostly with lobed bases...110

65

The round, crenate leaves with long petioles are characteristic. Plants are both aquatic and marginal; often are found as weeds in lawns. Some have peltate leaves. Although belonging to the wild carrot family with flowers in umbels, some species have an inflorescence with blossoms in small heads that are sessile at the end of a long stalk.

Fig. 68. *Hydrocotyle* (Umbelliferae) a. *H. verticillata;* b. *H. umbellata;* c. *H. americana* leaf.

flowers small, in a spadix, enclosed by a white spathe; plants
of marshes (Water Arum). Fig. 69......................*Calla*
This is the wild Calla Lily. The involucre or spathe is white. The
leaves are distinctly heart-shaped and arise in tufts from the end
of a creeping rhizome. Plants may be in shallow water or in wooded
swamps and are widely distributed across northern United States. The
rhizome is used by muskrats for food.

113b. Plants with leaves shaped otherwise and with different flowers.
....114

**114a. Leaves rhomboid or nearly circular, with serrate margins, aris-
ing either from rootstocks (basal) or from an erect stem; flowers
with yellow, petallike sepals (true petals lacking), a buttercup
type of bloom; plants of marshes (some species aquatic) (Marsh
Marigold). Fig. 70......................................*Caltha***
The flowers in this genus are relatively large and waxy, yellow
(or white) sepals (no petals). Included here is the familiar Marsh Marigold, each plant growing as a dense clump of large leaves. *C. natans*
is aquatic with the stems floating; occurs mostly in northern lakes.
C. palustris and its varieties is widely distributed; appears in reduced
form in the Subarctic.

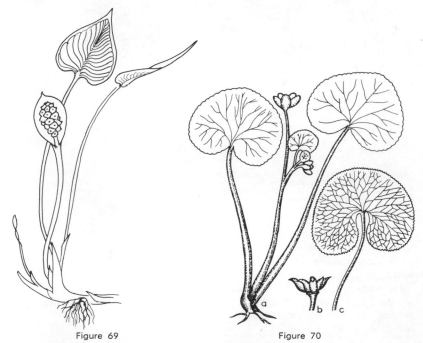

Figure 69   Figure 70

Fig. 69. *Calla palustris* (Araceae) Habit of plant.

Fig. 70. *Caltha palustris* (Ranunculaceae) a. Habit of plant; b. Follicles;
c. Another leaf shape.

114b. Leaves rhomboid-reniform; marginal lobes deep or shallow, often variable in shape and with lobings variable in form on the same plant (Buttercup). Fig. 71 ....*Ranunculus*

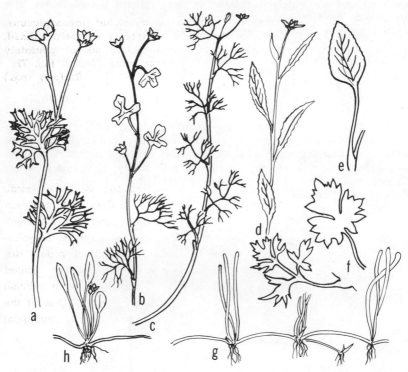

Fig. 71. *Ranunculus* (Ranunculaceae) a. *R. flabellaris*, portion of stem; b. *R. Purshii* showing two leaf forms; c. *R. aquatilis;* d. *R. ambigens;* e. *R. laxicaulis* leaf; f. *R. repens* leaves; g. *R. reptans*, a creeping species with linear leaves; h. *R. reptans* var. *ovalis*.

Species of *Ranunculus* are extremely variable in their leaf shapes and in the degree of lobings and divisions. Even the same plant may show different types of leaves. The completely submersed species have finely divided leaves which are either limp or somewhat rigid. The buttercup flowers are either white or yellow, and may open under water. Plant stems are conspicuously light (whitish) when seen under water. Many *Ranunculus* species are used by moose and aquatic birds for food.

115a. (109) Flowers with 4 petals, and 4 sepals (which often are deciduous), and 6 stamens; fruit a silique **116**

116a. Flowers greenish-white, small and somewhat inconspicuous; upper leaves simple but variously crenate or coarsely toothed, lower leaves pinnately lobed, often deeply so, or pinnately compound; (leaves sometimes alternate also) (Cress). Fig. 72..
....*Rorippa* (p.p.)

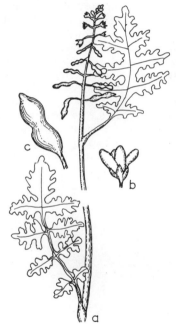

Plants in this genus have small, greenish-yellow flowers. Most are marginal; some grow emergent and erect, but *R. sylvestris* is prostrate. *R. palustris* is probably the most widely distributed species in eastern United States but *R. aquatica* (with whitish flowers) is also common. None of the species seems to have any biological importances.

Fig. 72. *Rorippa palustris* Var. (Cruciferae) a. Portion of plant with terminal raceme; b. Flower; c. Fruit.

117a. Upper leaves simple, elongate-elliptic, either finely or coarsely serrate, the lower leaves finely dissected and pinnately compound, forming lateral tufts which break away from the stem easily; flowers in a raceme, with fruits below and buds at the apex; fruit an oval capsule-silique which has but one chamber (Lake Cress). Fig. 73............................*Neobeckia*

This species often appears in a vegetative condition and does not show typical mustard family flower characters. When submersed the leaves are finely dissected. *Neobeckia* often becomes a weed and crowds out other more desirable or useful aquatic plants. Immature plants should be compared with young plants of *Megalodonta*. *Neobeckia* occurs in lagoons and along slowly flowing river shores.

Fig. 73. *Neobeckia aquatica* (Cruciferae) a. Habit showing finely dissected submersed leaves; b, c. submersed and emergent leaves.

117b. Plants without lower leaves finely dissected..............118

118a. Plants mostly erect (one species sprawling and rooted at nodes) but with unbranched stems; flowers relatively large (3 to 6 mm across), white or lavender; fruit an elongate slender, podlike silique which is flattened in cross section; plants with a basal leaf different in shape from the stem leaves (Bitter Cress). Fig. 74 ....*Cardamine*

Species of this genus are erect and little or not at all branched. Different species have characteristic and variable leaves, even on the same plant. There is a single, separate basal leaf which is always different in shape from those on the stem. Lower leaves are mostly pinnately lobed; the upper simple. Flowers are white or pink; the fruit a long, slender silique. Plants are sparsely scattered in a habitat; no biological importance is known.

Fig. 74. *Cardamine pratensis* Var. (Cruciferae) a. Habit of plant; b. Flower; c. Fruit.

118b. Plants prostrate and sprawling, often rank with hollow stems, much-branched; flowers small and several closely arranged in a compact panicle; fruit an elongate pod, round in cross section (Water Cress). Figure 75..........................*Nasturtium*

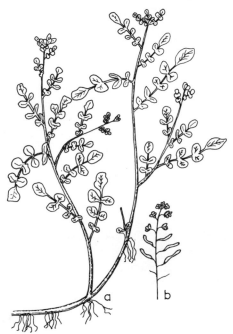

This is the well-known Water Cress, used as a salad. The plants are sprawling, usually in spring water and may be rank and hollow-stemmed. They often root from the stem nodes. There are several varieties and forms that are recognized and differentiated according to leaf form and size.

Fig. 75. *Nasturtium officinale* (Cruciferae)
a. Habit; b. Raceme.

119a. (115) Flowers yellow, with 5 petals and 5 sepals; pistils numerous; leaves oval or elliptic with serrate margins; plants often with palmately lobed leaves (Buttercup). Fig. 71....*Ranunculus*

120a. Flowers conspicuous, violet or purple; leaves cordate, on stems which also bear lobed leaves (Nightshade). Fig. 76.....*Solanum*

This plant is known as Nightshade or Bittersweet. The plants are sprawling and vinelike, often drooping over banks and growing in the water. Leaves are simple and heart-shaped or with one or two lobes, all on the same plant. The purple flowers produce clusters of red berries which are used by some birds.

Fig. 76. *Solanum Dulcamara* (Solanaceae) a. Branch; b. Flowers; c. Fruit.

120b. Flowers other colors, or colorless.........................121
121a. Flowers small, greenish or colorless, solitary in axils of leaves, with 3 calyx lobes but no petals; stamens 3; submersed leaves deeply incised (nearly compound), emergent leaves not lobed, but toothed along the margin (Mermaid Weed). Fig. 77........
....*Prosperinaca*

There are at least three species which are aquatic or semi-aquatic. The most common and widely distributed is *P. palustris* and its varieties. The variety *amblyogona* has coarsely serrate upper leaves and deeply lobed lower leaves, especially when submersed. Some species are known to be used by birds and muskrats.

121b. Flowers small, whitish, in heads which are arranged in umbels; leaves narrowly elongate, leathery, with coarse teeth or spiniferous margins; petioles hollow; fruit ovoid with ribs and oil tubes (Eryngo; Button Snakeroot). Fig. 78.............*Eryngium*

Species in this genus are marginal or only incidentally growing in water. Conical heads of flowers are arranged in compound umbels. One species, *E. prostratum* is procumbent; others are erect with spiny leaves.

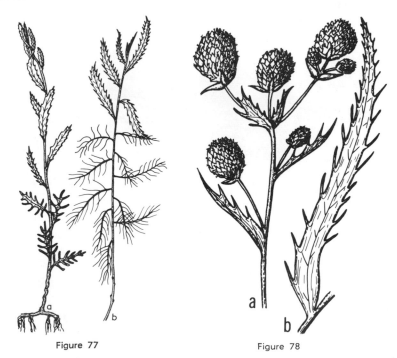

Figure 77   Figure 78

Fig. 77. *Prosperinaca* (Haloragaceae) a. *Prosperinaca* sp. habit; b. *P. palustris,* habit showing finely dissected leaves.

Fig. 78. *Eryngium* (Umbelliferae) a. Portion of plant; b. Leaf.

122a. (108) Leaf margins entire.................................123

122b. Leaf margins serrate (or sharply crenate)..................143

123a. Plants with a stipule or a stipular sheath at the base of the leaf, or covering each node, the sheath sometimes with a flaring collar..124

123b. Plants otherwise; without a sheath at each node...........126

124a. Leaves with a promnient midvein, and with lateral veins pinnately branching; stipular sheath on each node; plants sprawling or erect...125

124b. Leaves parallel-veined; stipule thin and attached to the leaf base, or forming a close sheath about the stem; leaves variously shaped, filiform, elliptic or broadly oval when submersed, with elliptic or oval floating leaves in some species (Pondweed). Fig. 46....................................*Potamogeton* (p.p.)

125a. Flowers in whorls in axils of leaves; sepals 6; leaves usually toothed (but entire in *Rumex verticillatus*); plants erect (Dock) Fig. 79..*Rumex*

Species of this genus are mostly marginal and are found in marshes and swamps; one occurs in tidal flats. *R. verticillatus* is commonly seen emergent in shallow water. Typical of the Polygonaceae there are stem sheaths at the base of the leaf petioles. The seeds are borne in rather dense terminal spikes and are much used by waterfowl.

Fig. 79. *Rumex verticillatus* (Polygonaceae) a. Habit; b. Leaf; c. Fruit.

125b. Flowers in spikes; leaves entire; sepals 4 or 5; aquatic species sprawling, terrestrial species erect (Smartweed). Fig. 80........ ....*Polygonum*

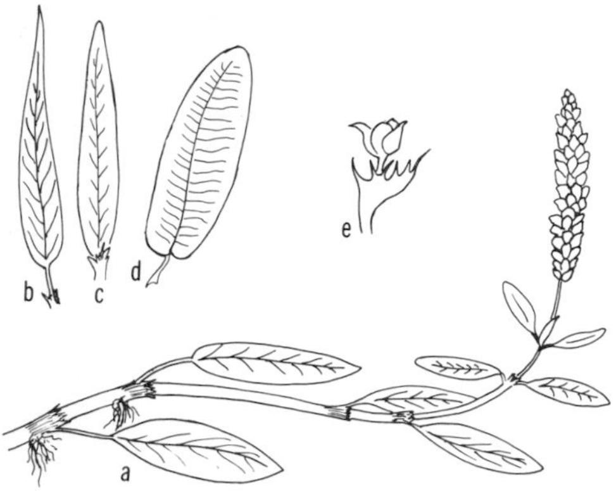

Fig. 80. *Polygonum* (Polygonaceae) a. *Polygonium natans;* b. *P. setaceum* leaf; c. *P. hydropiperoides* leaf; d. *P. coccineum* fa. *natans* leaf; e. Single flower and sheath.

Species of this genus may be entirely aquatic, marginal, or amphibious. The plants are so well-adapted to both an aquatic and a terrestrial existence that the same plant may have portions under water and some branches erect on land. Aquatic species have floating stems and leaves with emergent spikes of pink fowers. *P. natans* and *P. coccineum* are the most common species. They provide food for aquatic wildfowl and muskrats.

126a. (123) Leaves broadly oval, round or heart-shaped..........127

126b. Leaves elongate or elliptic-lanceolate......................130

127a. Leaves cordate or deltoid..................................128

127b. Leaves orbicular or round-reniform, sometimes peltate......129

128a. Leaves deltoid; plant a sprawling, semi-woody vine with purple flowers which are borne in leaf axils; stamens exerted from recurved petals; fruit a red berry; plants of lake margins (Nightshade). Fig. 76...................................*Solanum*
(Also see *Heteranthera limosa* (Fig. 94), leaves somewhat cordate.)

128b. Leaves deltoid to cordate; plants of bogs, not semi-woody vines; flowers small, numerous, in a spike enclosed by a white spathe (Water Arum). Fig. 69............................*Calla*

129a. (127) Leaves broadly oval to nearly round in the upper part of the plant, petioles short, blades deeply lobed and compound in the lower part; flowers small and white, in heads or racemose; plants sprawling and procumbent, often rank, the stems hollow; flowers with 4 petals and 6 stamens (Water Cress). Fig. 75... ....*Nasturtium*

129b. Leaves orbicular, broadly reniform or peltate, on long petioles from a procumbent stem; flowers in umbels; leaves usually serrate or crenate but sometimes nearly entire (Water Pennywort). Fig. 68.................................*Hydrocotyle*
(Also see *Heteranthera reniformis* (Fig. 94) leaves reniform.)

130a. (126) Flowers 2-lipped, the upper usually split or divided, solitary on a short stalk in the axils of leaves or bracts (Lobelia).
Fig. 81..*Lobelia*
This genus has several representatives in moist situations and one especially (*L. Dortmanna*) is emergent in shallow water. This species has a basal rosette of uniquely-shaped, fingerlike leaves. The showy cardinal flower *L. cardinalis* is not aquatic but is found in swamps and swales in the eastern half of the United States.

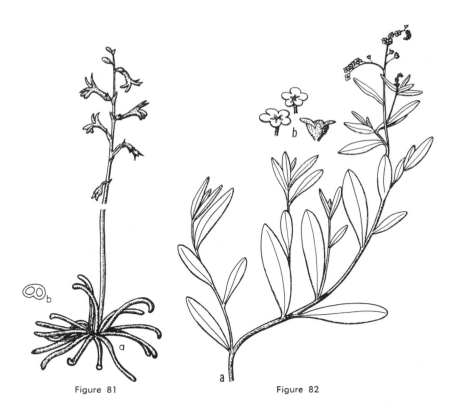

Figure 81   Figure 82

Fig. 81. *Lobelia Dortmanna* (Lobeliaceae) a. Habit of plant; b. Leaf in cross section (diagrammatic).

Fig. 82. *Myosotis* (Boraginaceae) a. Habit of plant; b. Flowers.

133a. Flowers arranged in close heads in the axils of bracts, the stalks of the heads arranged to form an umbel; leaves oblanceolate, sometimes entire but usually coarsely toothed (Eryngo). Fig. 78 ....Eryngium

133b. Flowers arranged otherwise............................134

134a. Flowers blue, salverform or rotate, with a yellow center (flowers sometimes white or pink), arranged to form a unilateral raceme; leaves linear or oblanceolate (sometimes spatulate) (Forget-me-not). Fig. 82..Myosotis

The familiar Forget-Me-Not is recognizable by its bright blue or pink flowers with yellow centers. Plants sprawl in shallow water or grow profusely in wet ditches and springy places. The numerous, dark seeds are used by birds.

134b. Flowers shaped and arranged otherwise..................135

135a. Leaves broadest at the base, narrowly to bluntly pointed, sessile and with or without ridges running down the stem from the leaf base; flowers yellow, conspicuous, solitary in the axils of leaves; calyx elongate (Water Primrose). Fig. 83.......Jussiaea

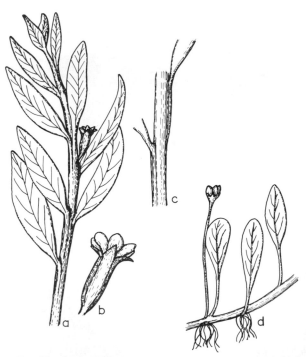

Fig. 83. *Jussiaea* (Onagraceae) a. *Jussiaea decurrens*, habit; b. Flower; c. Decurrent leaves; d. *J. diffusa*, portion of stem.

These plants live both in shallow water or sprawl on shores. Flowers are yellow and showy, with long, slender, inferior ovaries. The common *J. decurrens* has lanceolate leaves from the base of which ridges extend down the stem. *Jussiaea* is found mostly in midwest and southern states.

135b. Leaves tapered at the base, sometimes forming a petiole; flowers greenish or yellow; calyx short and urn-shaped; stems frequently rooting from the nodes; without wings or ridges extending down from leaf bases; leaves alternate in some but usually opposite (False Loosestrife). Fig. 51.............................*Ludwigia*

136a. (132) Flowers yellow.......................................137

136b. Flowers purple, blue or white............................138

137a. Leaves glandular-dotted; flowers yellow with purple dots; solitary in the axils of leaves or in a terminal raceme; petals united at the base of a superior ovary (Loosestrife). Fig. 44.....
....*Lysimachia*

137b. Leaves not glandular-dotted; flowers always solitary in the axils of leaves; ovary inferior; fruit an elongated capsule; plants rank herbs, up to 2 M high (Water Primrose). Fig. 83....*Jussiaea*

138a. (136) Low (1 to 2.5 dm high) herbs with a white (sometimes lavender) flowers arranged in a raceme or corymb; leaves simple on the upper part of the stem but pinnate, lobed or incised below (Bitter Cress). Fig. 74.............................*Cardamine*

138b. Plants otherwise...139

139a. Plants tall herbs, up to 2 M, semi-woody; leaves lanceolate, with the bases lobed, sessile; flowers purple with 6 petals, arranged in long, terminal spikes or solitary in the axils of leaves, or in whorls; capsule subcylindric (Spiked Loosestrife). Fig. 45.....
....*Lythrum*

139b. Plants not tall herbs, not semi-woody; leaves elliptic, nearly sessile with spines in the axils; flowers blue, rotate with 5 petals; capsule globular. Fig. 84.............................Hydrolea
In this genus there are ellipsoid, alternate leaves in the axils of which there are spines. Blue flowers in 2's and 3's also are borne in the leaf axils. The genus has two species; is confined to south central and southeastern states, growing in stream margins and swamps.

140a. (131) Coarse herbs, up to 2 M high; leaves lanceolate to nearly ovate, margins entire; flowers in panicles which are terminal, or axilary; dioecious; pistils with 2 to 5 long, plumose stigmas which persist; fruit a utricle (Water Hemp). Fig. 85.......Acnida
These are tall perennials, up to 2 M. The elliptical leaves have long petioles in the axils of which is a close panicle of flowers. Acnida is distributed along the Atlantic seaboard in marshes.

Figure 84   Figure 85

Fig. 84. *Hydrolea* (Hydrophyllaceae) a. *Hydrolea quadrivalvis*, habit; b. Flower; c. Fruit.

Fig. 85. *Acnida* (Amaranthaceae) a. *Acnida cannabina*, habit; b. Flower.

140b. Herbs otherwise; flowers not as above...................141

141a. Leaves slender, elongate (lanceolate or linear), entire but often on the same plant with leaves that may be serrate or toothed, or divided; flowers yellow; pistils numerous, forming achenes (Buttercup). Fig. 71...............................*Ranunculus*

141b. Plants otherwise...142

142a. Flowers solitary in the axils of leaves which are ovate or elliptic, margins smooth (False Loosestrife). Fig. 51.....*Ludwigia*

142b. Flowers forming a corymb or a terminal raceme (Bitter Cress). Fig. 74..*Cardamine*

143a. (122) Leaves circular in outline, orbicular or reniform, sometimes peltate 144

143b. Leaves elongate, lanceolate or long-elliptic...............146

144a. Leaves usually 3-lobed, sometimes very little divided and nearly entire, but with serrate or sharply crenate margins, variable on the same plant; flowers yellow or white, petals 5 or variable; pistils numerous, forming achenes when mature (Buttercup). Fig. 71 .... *Ranunculus (R. hederaceus et al.)*

144b. Plants otherwise..................................145

145a. Leaves circular or reniform, sometimes peltate, with coarsely or finely crenate margins, the round blades borne at the ends of long, vertical petioles from a subterranean, horizontal stem; flowers small, in umbels (sometimes much simplified); aquatic, with floating leaves, or terrestrial (Water Pennywort). Fig. 68... ....*Hydrocotyle*

145b. Leaves nearly round or deltoid (sometimes with the base lobed), the margins sharply serrate; flowers yellow, with 5 to 9 petal-like sepals (petals lacking); pistils numerous, the fruit as thin-walled pods (follicle) (Marsh Marigold). Fig. 70 ....*Caltha*

146a. (143) Plants submersed (some species with floating leaves); leaves alternate with a stipule, elongate-ellipsoid, slightly lobed at the base, narrowly or bluntly pointed at the apex; margin crisped and with minute serrations (Pondweed). Fig. 56....... ....*Potamogeton crispus*

146b. Plants otherwise.....................................147

147a. Plants with lower leaves deeply divided, incised or dissected (somewhat compound)....................................148

147b. Plants with lower leaves not lobed or divided.............151

148a. Lower leaves finely dissected and compound, upper leaves simple, small, lanceolate or elliptic, sessile; flowers small, white in terminal racemes (Lake Cress). Fig. 73..........*Neobeckia*

148b. Plants with leaves and flowers otherwise.................149

149a. Lower leaves pinnately lobed, deeply incised and nearly compound; upper leaves serrate with sharply pointed apices; flowers small, solitary in the axils of leaves; calyx with 3 lobes, no petals; fruits small nutlets, 3-sided (Mermaid Weed). Fig. 77.....
....*Prosperinaca*

149b. Plants otherwise...150

150a. Plants erect, little if at all branched; upper leaves narrowly elliptic to linear; lower leaves pinnately divided or compound; flowers small, greenish-yellow, in a terminal raceme; petals 4, stamens 6; fruit a globular silique, 2-chambered (Cress). Fig. 72
....*Rorippa*

150b. Plants sprawling or much-branched; leaves elliptic or elongate-spatulate; flowers conspicuous, yellow, solitary on a peduncle; pistils many, forming achenes (Buttercup). Fig. 71....*Ranunculus*

151a. (147) Flowers in dense heads, the heads stalked and arranged in umbels; leaves linear to lanceolate, lower coarsely serrate; plants tall and coarse (Eryngo). Fig. 78..............*Eryngium*

151b. Plants with a sheath at the base of the leaves; flowers pink-rose, or white, in whorls; leaves oval to lanceolate, crinkled and usually finely toothed (Dock). Fig. 79...................*Rumex*

152a. (106) Plants floating.....................................153

152b. Plants rooted in the soil; submersed, emergent, or on shores..156

153a. Leaves broad, lettucelike blades on a short, thick petiole from a thick stem that bears numerous, fine roots; stems proliferating by stolons and giving rise to secondary rosettes; (plants sometimes stranded on muddy shores); plants of tropical waters (Water Lettuce). Fig. 86................................*Pistia*

This plant is floating and lettucelike. Stranded plants will grow well on muddy shores. The flowers are on a spadix with a lightcolored spathe. The species is tropical or subtropical, occurring in the Gulf states and the extreme southwest United States. In some parts of the world *Pistia* becomes a serious nuisance to navigation (Panama Canal, e.g.).

Fig. 86. *Pistia stra-tioides* (Araceae) Habit.

153b. Leaves otherwise......................................154

154a. Leaves cordate or broadly elliptic.........................155

154b. Leaf blades triangular in outline, pinnately lobed, or twice pinnate, arising from a floating rootstock that bears numerous roots; compound leaves producing sporangia on the under side, the sporangia arranged in one or two rows on one or both sides of the longitudinal vein; (plants sometimes stranded on muddy shores); plants of tropical and subtropical waters (Floating Fern). Fig. 87 . . . .*Ceratopteris*

This species and *C. Deltoides* are large, floating ferns of the Gulf region in the United States. The sterile leaves are triangular in outline and lobed; are borne in a rosette. The fertile fronds are pinnately compound. *C. pteridoides* has inflated petioles.

Fig. 87. *Ceratopteris pteridoides* (Parkeriaceae) Habit of plant (redrawn from Muenscher).

155a. Leaves cordate, subcordate to broadly elliptic, up to 4 cm wide; blades with about 25 parallel veins all arising from the base of the blade and with conspicuous cross veins; blades spongy on the underside; flowers monoecious, staminate and pistillate both enclosed in a spathe with 2 bracts (Frogbit). Fig 88 . . . .
. . . .*Limnobium*

This plant may be either floating, or attached in mud. The heart-shaped leaves have characteristic, cross-hatched venation. It occurs along the Mississippi and Ohio rivers in central United States and along the Atlantic seaboard. The solitary flowers are on a recurved peduncle arising from a spathe.

Fig. 88. *Limnobium spongia* (Hydrocharitaceae) Habit.

83

155b. **Leaves with ovate or cordate blades on petioles which have an inflated, saclike bladder, the petioles arising from a short stem that proliferates by a stolon, secondary rosettes formed from the stolons; flowers violet to white and purple, irregular (somewhat zygomorphic), on a spike which arises from within a 2-valved spathe (Water Hyacinth). Fig. 89**.....................*Eichhornia*

This is the beautiful and infamous Water Hyacinth that dominates the water ways of the tropics and subtropics. The flowers are showy, light purple and white, arranged in a spike. The leaves have swollen petioles, forming floats that give great buoyancy. Plants multiply rapidly vegetatively wherever they become established. Water Hyacinth is used by aquatic animals for food, including the marine Manatee (Sea Cow).

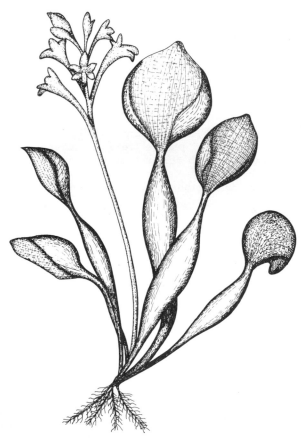

Fig. 89. *Eichhornia crassipes* (Pontederiaceae) Habit.

156a. (152) Small plants of bogs and acid, sandy soil; insectivorous; leaf blades circular or oval or filiform, bearing stiff hairs with glandular tips; leaves reddish; flowers white, in a panicle (Sundew). Fig. 90...*Drosera*

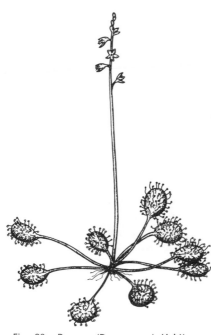

These small plants occupy *Sphagnum* bogs and sandy lake shores. The leaf blades and petioles bear glandular hairs. The sticky fluid produced by the hairs ensnares small insects and the hairs, being sensitive to touch, bend over and down, holding the insect until digestion has taken place, after which they regain their original position. It is thought that this type of nutrition aids in supplying nitrogen which is scarce or absent in the substrate where Sundews live. One of the most common species is *D. rotundifolia* with circular or broadly oval leaves. *D. linearis* has long, slender, filiform leaves with scarcely any blade.

Fig. 90. *Drosera* (Droseraceae) Habit.

156b. Plants otherwise...157

157a. Leaves linear, fleshy, in a compact rosette, without petioles; flowering shoot naked, bearing 2-lipped flowers (Lobelia). Fig. 81 ....*Lobelia*

157b. Plants with leaves otherwise...........................158

158a. Leaves sagittate...159

158b. Leaves with other shapes, orbicular, elliptic, (broadly elliptic in some), elongate-oval, lanceolate, linear, or triangular and pinnately lobed...161

159a. Blades sharply arrow-shaped, with apex and basal lobes sharply pointed, with 3 prominent veins, a midvein and one extending into either lobe; petiole long and fleshy; flowers numerous, small, on a spike enclosed by a spathe (Arrow Arum). Fig. 91..
....*Peltandra*

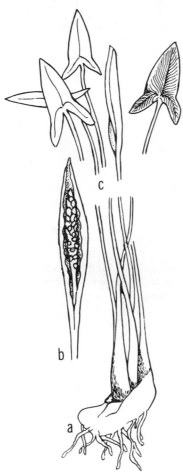

This is the widely distributed and familiar Arrow Arum of bogs, swamps and ditches. The leaves are superficially like those of *Sagittaria* but are readily differentiated by three prominent veins in the blade, one into either lobe, and one median. The inflorescence is distinctive, being a spadix with a spathe. This species is more common in the eastern half of the United States.

Fig. 91. *Peltandra virginica* (Araceae) a. Basal portion of plant; b. Spadix and spathe; c. Leaves and spathe.

159b. Leaves differently shaped and veined; flowers arranged otherwise 160

160a. Leaves with sagittate blades (elongate to linear when young and/or submersed); the petioles fleshy, veins several, of equal prominence, radiating from the base of the blade; flowers in whorls on a naked scape which is not inflated; lower flowers staminate or pistillate only, the upper flowers perfect; petals and sepals 3 (Arrowhead; Delta Potato). Fig. 92......
....*Sagittaria*
Whereas most species have arrow-shaped blades, some have linear or ribbonlike leaves. Also some leaves are elliptical when plants are young and submersed but become sagittate in age. Others have grass-like leaves below the surface and elliptical blades when emergent. Species are submersed or emergent and form meadows in sloughs, lagoons and bayous. *S. latifolia* is the most widely distributed species. The plants bear underground tubers which are much sought after by ducks. The tubers (Delta Potatoes) are also used by Man for food. In especially favorable habitats *Sagittaria* may grow waist-high.

Fig. 92. *Sagittaria* (Alismaceae) a. *Sagittaria cuneata;* b. *S. subulata;* c,f. *S. cristata;* d. Single flower; e. Head of fruits; g. Single nutlet; h. Leaf of *S. cuneata.*

160b. Leaves with sagittate blades but with the lateral margins strongly convex; veins arranged palmately from the base of the blade; flowering scape inflated and the pedicels of the flowers thick; lower flowers perfect, upper flowers with stamens only; sepals persisting and closely enclosing the fruits which consist of nutlets. Fig. 93............................. *Lophotocarpus*

In this genus the leaves are much the same in shape as *Sagittaria* and the plants grow in the same types of habitat. Leaves are often more lanceolate than sagittate. In *Sagittaria* the *lower* flowers in the raceme are pistillate, whereas in *Lophotocarpus* they are perfect.

Fig. 93. *Lophotocarpus* (Alismaceae) a. Portion of plant showing leaves and flowers; b. Fruit (nutlet) c. Lower, perfect flower.

161a. (158) Leaves cordate or reniform, sometimes with basal lobes reduced. 162

161b. Leaves not cordate or reniform, but orbicular, elliptical, elongate-lanceolate, or spatula-shaped; or broadly oval, ribbonlike and linear 166

162a. Plants submersed; leaves broadly reniform, basal on a slender, creeping stem (but often alternate on an erect stem); flowers

usually solitary (sometimes several), in a spathe; leaves without a distinct midvein but with parallel veins from the leaf base (Mud Plantain). Fig. 94...............*Heteranthera* (p.p.)

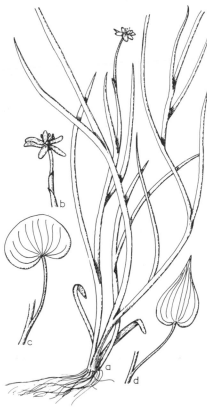

Heteranthera dubia is the most widely distributed of four species in the United States. Plants often superficially resemble some *Potamogeton*. The leaves in some are linear and alternate but have no stipules. When in flower *Heteranthera* is readily differentiated by its starlike, trimerous flowers. Plants are used as food by ducks.

Fig. 94. *Heteranthera* (Pontederiaceae) a. *Heteranthera dubia*, habit; b. Single flower; c. *Heteranthera reniformis*, leaf; d. *H. limosa*.

163a. Leaves broadly heart-shaped, the veins radiating from the base of the blade, several close together in the mid-region, forming a somewhat prominent rib; leaves clustered and located at the end of a prostrate rootstock; flowers in a spike and enclosed in a white spathe; plants of marshes and lagoon margins (Water Arum). Fig. 69...*Calla*

163b. Leaves and flowers otherwise.............................164

164a. Leaves somewhat heart-shaped (but mostly lance-shaped) on long, erect, emergent petioles; blades with parallel veins, divergent from the base of the blade; flowers purple or blue, on a spike with a small basal spathe; stem a thickened pad, bearing many roots (Pickerelweed). Fig. 95................*Pontederia*

This species has characteristic lance-shaped blades on long petioles with parallel venation. The flowering scape bears showy, bluish-purple blooms. The leaf petioles and flowering shoot are erect and emergent. Plants are used by muskrats and the seeds are eaten by many birds.

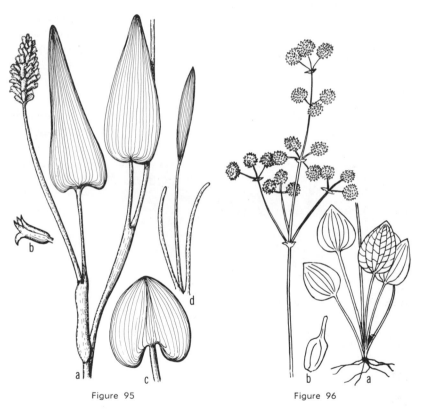

Figure 95   Figure 96

Fig. 95. *Pontederia cordata* (Pontederiaceae) a. Habit of upper portion of plant; b. Single flower; c, d. Variation in shape of leaves.

Fig. 96. *Echinodorus* (Alismaceae) a. Inflorescence (scape) and basal portion of *Echinodorus cordifolius*; b. Fruit.

164b. Plants otherwise..165

165a. Leaves elliptic to slightly heart-shaped, blade with 25 or more parallel veins from the base, with many cross veinlets at right angles sometimes purple on the underside; plants proliferating by stolons; flowers monoecious, the staminate 3 to 10, in a spathe composed of 2 bracts; pistillate solitary or 2 in the same spathe; plants usualy floating but sometimes attached (Frogbit). Fig. 88 . . . . *Limnobium*

165b. Leaves distinctly cordate, the blade with 7 veins radiating from the base, the veinlets at right angles and forming rectangular spaces; flowers perfect on a pedicel which is part of a compound panicle (sometimes a simple one); flowers with up to 30 stamens and numerous pistils which form achenes that have an apical beak (Burhead). Fig. 96 . . . . *Echinodorus*

In this genus the leaves are heart-shaped and basal. The flowers form heads, borne on the branches of a panicle. The habit of growth is much like that of *Alisma* but differs by having flowers in heads rather than in rings about a receptacle. The fruits are used by waterfowl.

166a. (161) Leaves fleshy, somewhat triangular in outline, becoming pinnately lobed or compound in age; ferns with sporangia on the back of pinnately compound, fertile fronds when mature, the sterile leaves broad, up to 4 dm long, the fertile pinnae narrow; margins of fronds bearing buds or developing plantlets; plants of tropical or subtropical waters (Floating Fern, Horn Fern). Fig. 87 . . . . *Ceratopteris*

166b. Plants otherwise; not ferns 167

167a. Leaves round in outline or somewhat rhomboid, sagittate or peltate 168

167b. Leaves elliptic, elongate, lanceolate, oblong or ovate-elliptic, sometimes large, up to 3 feet long; spatulate or linear 170

168a. Leaves rhomboid or sometimes triangular, or nearly circular all on the same plant with leaves which are sagittate; flowers small, on a spike enclosed by a spathe; blades with 3 prominent veins, a midvein and a downwardly directed lateral vein into either lobe (Arrow Arum). Fig. 91 . . . . *Peltandra*

168b. Plants otherwise 169

169a. Leaves circular, orbicular, sometimes peltate, with crenate margins; blades on long petioles from subterranean stems; flowers small, in umbels (Water Pennywort). Fig. 68 . . . . *Hydrocotyle*

169b. Leaves nearly circular but mostly broadly reniform; margins serrate (entire in some species); flowers mostly solitary or 2, 3 together on a flowering shoot, sepals yellow or white (petals lacking) (Marsh Marigold). Fig. 70 . . . . *Caltha*

170a. (167) Plants low herbs with lanceolate or elongate-elliptic leaves on long petioles, margins crenulate, arising from the end of a horizontal, perennial rhizome; flowers solitary, white; leaves mostly in a basal rosette, but with some leaves on the stem; plants of marshes and sandy soil shores (Violet). Fig. 97...*Viola*

Although not truly aquatic some species of violet grow in marshes and on sandy shores. *V. lanceolata*, a white-flowered species is widely distributed in eastern United States.

Fig. 97. *Viola lanceolata* (Violaceae) Habit.

170b. Plants otherwise; leaves shaped differently.................171

171a. Plants dwarfed, up to 4 or 5 cm high; stem creeping, white runners giving rise to tufts of spatula-shaped leaves (sometimes linear in certain species) rounded at the tips; petioles long, slender, broadened apically into an elliptic blade; flowers solitary on simple, recurved peduncles (Mudwort). Fig. 98......*Limosella*

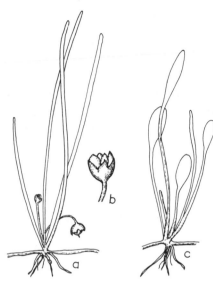

Species in this genus are dwarf plants with linear, flat or threadlike leaves. They live in mud; have runners which give rise to trufts of leaves, and root frequently. Each plant has three or four nodding stalks from the base that bear a single, small flower. Plants are rare but *L. aquatica* is widely distributed.

Fig. 98. *Limosella* (Scrophulariaceae) a. *Limosella subulata*, habit; b. Single flower; c. *L. aquatica*, habit.

171b. Plants larger; with leaves different........................172

172a. Leaf blades broadly elliptic or ovate on short, thick petioles; leaves up to 1 M long; inflorescence a spadix with a yellow or purple-spotted spathe.....................................173

172b. Leaves otherwise, smaller; stem often cormlike; inflorescence not a spadix..174

173a. **Leaves broadly oval, on a short petiole, up to 6 dm long;
spadix short at first, enclosed in a purple-spotted or striped
spathe, elongating at maturity and bearing a globular or oval
head of fruits, the spadix appearing before the leaves; plants
with a squnk odor (Skunk Cabbage). Fig. 99 ..... Symplocarpus**

In this genus the leaves are broad, ovoid and basal arising from
a perennial rootstock. The flowers are borne in a spadix and inclosed
by a purplish spotted spathe, the spadix often appearing before the
leaves in the spring. The common name Skunk Cabbage is derived
from the fact that the leaves when crushed give off a distinct skunk-
like odor. Plants inhabit swamps and marshes. S. *foetidus* is distributed throughout the eastern half of the United States.

Figure 99   Figure 100

Fig. 99. *Symplocarpus foetidus* (Araceae) Habit.
Fig. 100. *Lysichitum americanum* (Araceae) Habit.

173b. **Leaves broadly elliptic to oblanceolate and broadly oval, up
to 1 M in length, the blades borne on stout petioles; spadix
short and scarcely emergent at first, enclosed in a yellow
spathe, eventually becoming elongate and clublike, bearing a
cylindrical spike of fruits; plants with a skunk odor (Yellow
Skunk Cabbage). Fig. 100 .... Lysichitum**

This is the Yellow Skunk Cabbage, a plant of bogs and marshes in northwestern North America. The leaves are broadly oval and large, up to a meter in length, all basal and arising from a rhizome. The spadix is enclosed at first in a yellow spathe but later enlarges remarkably and forms a club 3 or 4 dm in length.

174a. (172) **Leaves elongate-lanceolate to somewhat spatulate, on a long, slender petiole which is inflated at the base, the blade with 3 veins or nerves, leaves all basal and arising from cormlike rootstocks; flowers white, with 3 sepals and petals, arranged in a panicle, 6 carpels forming achenes; leaves either submersed or with floating blades (Damasonium). Fig. 101....** *Damasonium*

This is one of two genera in the Alismaceae in which the pistils (achenes) are arranged in a ring about the flower receptacle. The basal leaves are similar to those of *Alisma* in shape. The achenes, unlike *Alisma*, are conspicuously ridged on the *back*. Further, the petals are toothed rather than entire. Plants grow in shallow water (become emergent) or on shores.

Figure 101   Figure 102

Fig. 101. *Damasonium californicum* (Alismaceae) Habit.

Fig. 102. *Alisma plantago-aquatica* (Alismaceae) a. Habit; b. Flowers; c. Fruits arranged around the receptacle; d. Nutlet of *Alisma gramineus*; e. Leaf of *A. gramineus*; f. *A. plantago-aquatica*, another leaf shape.

174b. **Plants otherwise**..**175**

175a. Leaves oblong-elliptic or sometimes lanceolate, rarely nearly cordate; blades with 1 prominent midvein and several lateral subparallel veins (3 on each side of the midvein), leaves all arising basically from a cormlike stem; petioles often reddish; flowers small in compound panicles, with 3 white petals; numerous pistils on a flat receptacle, forming achenes which have a keel along one side and flattened on the other two sides (Water Plantain). Fig. 102 . . . . *Alisma*

The most common species is *Alisma plantago-aquatica* with cordate or broadly elliptic leaves. *A. gramineus* has narrowly elliptic or linear leaves and is less common. Like *Damasonium*, the achenes are arranged in a ring about the receptacle, the achenes being smooth rather than ridged on the back, but with a keel on the side. Birds make limited use of the fruits for food.

175b. Plants otherwise 176

176a. Leaves shaped somewhat like those of *Alisma*, distinctly elliptic to lanceolate, the blade with about 10 longitudinal, subparallel veins of equal prominence, leaves all arising basally from a short, thick rootstock; flowers many, small on a spike which is naked (inconspicuous spathe); plants on shores or in shallow water (Golden Club). Fig. 103 . . . . *Orontium*

This species occurs in eastern United States especially along the coast where plants occupy ponds and tidal flats. The leaves are elongate-lanceolate on long petioles and the spadix is elongate-cylindric up to 2 dm long, arising from an inconspicuous spathe. Its yellow color accounts for the common name.

176b. Plant with leaves and flowers otherwise 177

177a. Leaves linear, with some lanceolate blades which in some varieties are more often spatulate or elongate-cordate, all basal from a horizontal rootstock, the flowers funnelform, 2-lipped, blue-purple in a terminal cluster on a flowering shoot which bears a single head; petioles stout, erect, emergent in shallow water (Pickerelweed). Fig. 95 . . . . *Pontederia*

177b. Plants with different leaves and flowers 178

178a. Plants submersed, leaves ovate, or with parallel margins and without a distinct midrib, basal from near the end of a creeping rootstock (but often on the erect stem, and alternate); flowers solitary or 2, 3 together with a spathe (Mud Plantain). Fig. 94 . .
. . . . *Heteranthera*

178b. Plants otherwise 179

179a. Leaves, especially when young and submersed, elongate-ellipsoid or lanceolate to nearly linear, emergent; or older leaves sagittate, the petiole expanded toward the base and sheathing; flowers in whorls of 3, either on short stalks from a shoot, or on elongate stalks which are arranged in a whorl; lower flowers pistillate, upper flowers staminate (Arrowhead; Delta Potato). Fig. 92 . . . . *Sagittaria*

179b. Leaves lanceolate or occurring as phyllodia when submersed, emergent leaves cordate; veins several, prominent, parallel from the base of the blade; flowers in an open panicle, the verticils bearing flowers in whorls; all flowers perfect; petals 3, pistils numerous, forming achenes with a nearly erect apical beak (Burhead). Fig. 96.............................. *Echinodorus*

180a. (46) Leaves basal, appearing as clumped, several arising from a subterranean rootstock or rhizome.......................181

180b. Leaves alternate, opposite or whorled, arising from the stem (although there may be some leaves at or near the base of the stem)...183

181a. Leaves palmately compound.............................182

181b. Leaves twice pinnately compound, a fern with both fertile and sterile leaves, or with one portion of the leaf fertile and another section sterile; plants of marshes, up to 1 M tall (Royal Fern). Fig. 104...*Osmunda*

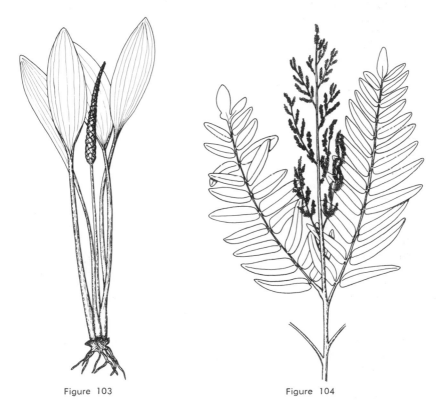

Figure 103   Figure 104

Fig. 103. *Orontium aquaticum* (Araceae) Habit.

Fig. 104. *Osmunda* (Osmundaceae) Habit of *Osmunda regalis* leaves and sporophylls.

This fern forms large clumps in swamps and bogs. The leaves are pinnately compound. Some species have sporangia borne on separate, chlorophylles leaves; others have special pinnae of vegetative leaves differentiated as reproductive leaflets. Rootstocks are perennial and long-lived, sometimes building sizeable mounds in swampy lands.

182a. Leaves 2 or 3 from the end of a spongy rootstock; flowers white or pink, in a raceme on a leafless stalk; corolla funnelform, hairy; plants of marshes, especially in acid bogs with *Sphagnum* (Bog Bean, Buck Bean). Fig. 105 . . . . *Menyanthes*

This species has relatively large, characteristically 3-lobed, compound basal leaves. The many-flowered stalk bears showy, white blooms. The fruit is a capsule, containing a number of brown seeds. The only species is widely distributed over the world, occurring in the eastern and far western parts of the United States.

Fig. 105. *Menyanthes trifoliata* (Menyanthaceae; Gentianaceae) a. Habit of portion of plant; b. single flower.

182b. Leaves 2 or 3 (rarely solitary) from a slender rhizome or a shortened rootstock, blade quadrifoliate on a slender petiole,

especially long when submersed; plants short and matted when growing on shore; a nutletlike sporocarp borne laterally on the petioles when mature (Pepperwort). Fig. 106........*Marsilea*

This is an aquatic fern which has 4-foliate, palmately compound leaves—appearing as an *Oxalis* or Shamrock. The petioles are long, especially when plants are aquatic. On land the plants are short-tufted, forming a turf. When plants are mature the petioles bear stalked sporangiophores which are used by water fowl. There are four species in the United States, of which *M. vestita* in the western half of the United States, and *M. quadrifolia* in the east are the most common. Plants often form a "lawn" on lakes shores, reproducing rapidly by proliferation from horizontal rootstocks.

Fig. 106. *Marsilea quadrifolia* (Marsileaceae) a. Habit of plant; b. Sporocarp luteral on leaf petiole; c. Leaf.

184a. Leaves compound, sparsely dichotomously branched to form
thick, linear segments which are either tapering or flattened,
olive or reddish-green; plants of streams, attached to rocks
(River Weed). Fig. 107.............................*Podostemum*

This is a distinctly shaped plant attached to
rocks in flowing water. The leaves are stemlike,
dichotomously divided, either long and slender,
or short with flattened extensions. Stipules are
frequently present at the base of the long petioles.
P. ceratophyllum, with several varieties is the only
species, occurring in western and southern United
States. Plants are of biological importance in
aquatic habitats, especially in reference to insect
life histories.

Fig. 107. *Podoste-
mum ceratophyllum*
(Podostemaceae) a.
Habit of plant; b.
Spathe and flower.

184b. Plants with leaves otherwise............................185

185a. Leaves palmately compound, 4-parted blades on long petioles,
solitary from slender, horizontal rhizomes; (leaves somewhat
tufted, 2 or more arising together or seemingly so from the same
point on the rhizome); leaflets triangular, the margins entire
(rarely somewhat undulate) (Pepperwort). Fig. 106.....*Marsilea*

185b. Leaves pinnately compound or abundantly dichotomously divided
....186

186a. Leaves finely dissected into threadlike divisions............199

186b. Leaves pinnately compound; blades flat although segments may
be narrow; not finely dissected into filiform divisions.......187

187a. Leaves once-pinnate, with leaflets sometimes again deeply lobed.
....188

187b. Leaves twice-pinnate....................................197

188a. Leaves all basal, in a rosette; leaflets obovate or lanceolate, silvery below; plants of marshes and beaches; flowers yellow (Cinquefoil). Fig. 108......................*Potentilla anserina*
This species has tufts of basal, pinnately compound leaves growing from runners. The plants occupy beaches, often among sedges. Flowers are yellow and buttercuplike. Because of their habit of growth these plants are useful in soil-binding and in beach-building.

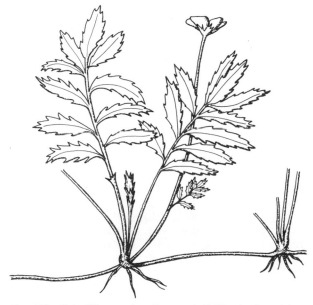

Fig. 108. *Potentilla anserina* (Rosaceae) Habit, showing stolon.

188b. Leaves borne on procumbent or erect stems, not all basal...189

189a. Plants with erect stems; branches none or few..............192

189b. Plants procumbent or sprawling, often much-branched......190

190a. **Leaves usually with 5 leaflets, that are elliptical or oblong lanceolate, the margins serrate, petioles with stipules which sheath or clasp the stem; petioles red-purple; flowers solitary, purple and showy (Cinquefoil). Fig. 109.....*Potentilla palustris***

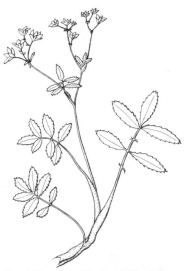

This species sprawls on shores and into the water, especially within reed beds and among cattail. The leaves are palmately compound with purple petioles. The flowers also are purple. Both plants and seeds are known to be used by browsing animals and birds.

Fig. 109. *Potentilla palustris* (Rosaceae) Habit of plant.

195a. **Fruit ellipsoid or oval, with 1 oil tube between pairs of ridges; plants low, 0.5 to 1.8 dm tall; leaflets narrowly oblong with serrate margins (sometimes entire) (Dropwort; Hog-fennel). Fig. 110** .... *Oxypolis*

This species occurs in western United States, especially in sub-alpine regions, either in shallow water or in grassy bogs. Three other species are found in eastern and southern states. The plants have fascicles of fleshy roots. *Oxypolis* is often distinctive because at least some of the upper leaves are reduced to spikelike phyllodes (blades lacking). The basal leaves are pinnately compound with five to 13 leaflets. They occur along streams and in marshes.

195b. **Fruit oblong, with 2 oil tubes between pairs of ridges; flowers white in compound umbels; lower submersed leaves highly dissected (Water Parsnip). Fig. 111** .... *Sium*

This species is nearly always aquatic and emergent; many times growing in meadows and marshes where there is standing water. The lower leaves are variously divided, sometimes filiform, whereas the upper, emergent leaves have broad, pinnately compound blades. Whereas the plants probably play a role in aquatic biology as an aerator there seems to be no use by animals or birds. The species is widely distributed over the United States.

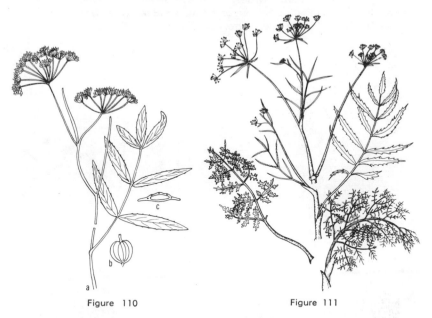

Figure 110   Figure 111

Fig. 110. *Oxypolis occidentale* (Umbelliferae) a. Habit of plant portion; b. Fruit; c. Cross section of fruit.

Fig. 111. *Sium suave* (Umbelliferae) Habit showing variations in leaf divisions.

103

196a. (194) Flowers yellowish-green, in a raceme or panicle (Cress). Fig. 72 . . . . *Rorippa*

196b. Flowers white (or lavender), in a raceme (Bitter Cress). Fig. 74 . . . . *Cardamine*

197a. (187) Plants prostrate or procumbent, rooting from the nodes: leaves mostly twice-pinnate (occasionally some once-pinnate); the leaflets broadly ovate with coarsely serrate margins, 2 to 6 cm long; flowers white, in terminal, compound umbels; fruit oblong cylindric, with 1 oil tube between each pair of ridges (Water Celery). Fig. 112 . . . . *Oenanthe*

This is a distinctly aquatic genus in the family. The plants are mostly procumbent but have erect branches. The leaves are twice-compound. *O. saementosa* is found in habitats along the northwest Pacific coast.

197b. Plants erect 198

198a. Tall, rank plants up to 3 M high; leaves coarse, thick, twice-pinnate lower leaves sometimes ternate), broad and up to 4 dm long; leaflets lanceolate or linear-elliptic; coarsely serrate, up to 8 cm long; fruit globular, but laterally compressed; umbels numerous, their involucres relatively small and inconspicuous, or lacking (Water Hemlock). Fig. 113 . . . . *Cicuta*

This species is more widely distributed than *C. maculata*, both species growing in shallow water or in swales. Like *Oxypolis* there are fleshy roots. Plants are large, usually erect with dense umbels of

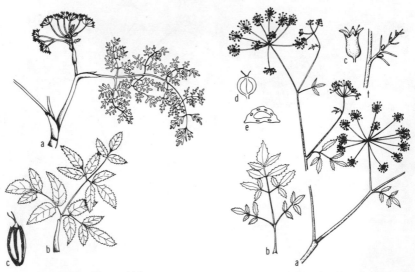

Figure 112   Figure 113

Fig. 112. *Oenanthe* (Umbelliferae) a. Habit of upper portion of plant; b. Lower leaf; c. Fruit.

Fig. 113. *Cicuta bulbifera* (Umbelliferae) a. Habit of upper portion of plant; b. Lower leaf; c. Flower; d. Fruit; e. Cross section of fruit.

white flowers, and with twice-pinnately or ternately compound leaves. This is the famous Water Hemlock with poisonous roots.

198b. Plants up to 1½ M tall, usually much less; leaves thin, the divisions spreading widely, the leaflets oval or ovate-lanceolate; the umbel of flowers relatively large with 20 to 45 stalks, variable in length; involucre conspicuous (Angelica). Fig. 114....*Angelica*

In this genus the leaves are twice-pinnate or ternately compound, and with leaflets broader than in *Cicuta*. The sheaths at the base of the leaves are relatively long, up to 10 cm, whereas in *Cicuta* they are only 3 cm or less. The plants are tall, up to 2 M. *Angelica* is one of the genera in the Umbelliferae which has fruits with winged ribs. Like *Cicuta*, *Angelica* grows in marshes and along stream courses.

199a. (186) Plants floating......................................200
199b. Plants attached, submerged or on the shore.................201
200a. Stems stout, inflated, submersed portion bearing uncrowded, pinnately compound leaves, the emersed portion with a rosette of much-inflated branches, bearing whorls of small flowers (Featherfoil). Fig. 115.................................*Hottonia*

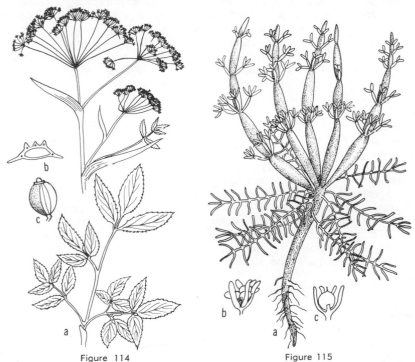

Figure 114   Figure 115

Fig. 114. *Angelica* (Umbelliferae) a. Leaves and umbels in upper portion of plant; b. Cross section of fruit; c. Fruit.

Fig. 115. *Hottonia inflata* (Primulaceae) a. Habit of plant; b. Flower; c. Fruit.

This is a unique, floating plant (rarely stranded). The thick, vertical axial stem has a rosette of inflated branches at the surface that bear whorls of flowers. The leaves are submersed and pinnately compound (somewhat rootlike), the divisions linear. In the United States the species is found in southern regions and in the Ohio valley.

200b. **Stems long, threadlike and lax, bearing alternate or opposite, finely dissected and dichotomously divided leaves that bear numerous animal-catching bladders (Bladderwort). Fig. 116.....** ....*Utricularia*

201a. **(199) Leaves dichotomously or irregular dissected to form thread-like divisions, the divisions sometimes flattened and narrowly ribbonlike**..**202**

201b. **Leaves pinnately divided to form threadlike divisions........204**

202a. **Leaves (and stem branches) bearing animal-trapping bladders, the bladders at first green and purplish, becoming black in age; flowers yellow or purple, 2-lipped, the lower lip with a spur; the flowers borne on erect, naked scapes (except for bracts at the base of flower peduncles); plants attached, anchored but without roots, or, more often, floating freely and drifting just beneath the water surface (Bladderwort). Fig. 116................**Utricularia*
This genus is unique in its possession of bladders on finely dissected leaves, or on special, slender branches, all of which are dichotomously divided. A few species have a horizontal, subterranean stem, a few erect branches and flowering scapes. The plants are rootless but may lie on the bottom, more often are freely floating. Flowers are yellow or purple. *Utricularia* is often found in acid or soft-water habitats, although they do occur in basic waters. The bladders have valvelike "doors" which open to allow small animals to enter. Animals are digested and contribute to the nitrogen metabolism of the plant. The bladders are green at first, become purple and then black in age as insect remains collect in them. The plants are often coated with adherent or epiphytic algae. Fourteen or 15 species are widely distributed in the United States.

202b. **Leaves without bladders; plants otherwise.................203**

203a. **Leaves alternate, but rarely so, mostly opposite or whorled, without a sheath at the base of the petiole, primary divisions palmate, successive divisions dichotomous; stem often bearing oblong, peltate, floating leaves; flowers solitary, white with 3 sepals and 3 petals, carpels 3 or 4; flowers borne on a slender peduncle in the axils of some upper leaves; fruit a 1-seeded, nutlike follicle (Fanwort, Parrot Feather). Fig. 33.....**Cabomba*

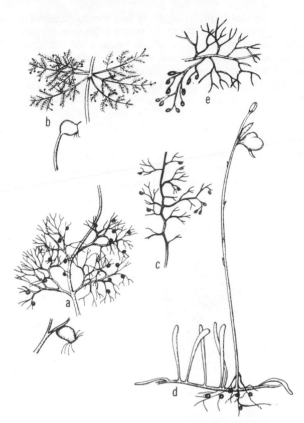

Fig. 116. *Utricularia* (Lentihulariaceae) a. *Utricularia vulgaris* leaves; b. *U. purpurea* leaves and bladder; c. *U. minor* leaves; d. *U. cornuta*, habit; e. *U. intermedia* branches with bladders.

203b. Leaves alternate (rarely opposite), ultimate divisions dichotomous although the first divisions are palmate; plants sometimes with upper or floating leaves lobed or not so finely dissected as the submersed leaves which have a sheath at the base; flowers white or yellow, petals 5 (or indefinite in number); pistils numerous, forming achenes (Buttercup). Fig. 71 . . . . *Ranunculus*

204a. (201). Plants stout with hollow stems; the basal leaves in a rosette (or whorl), finely divided, the upper leaves pinnately compound or twice-pinnate, the leaflets sometimes elliptic or lanceolate in some forms; base of petiole expanded to form a somewhat clasping sheath; flowers small, white, in a terminal umbel; plants emergent or on boggy shores (Water Parsnip). Fig. 111 . . . . *Sium*

204b. Plants not as above **205**

205a. Plants erect (at least in part), or trailing in the water, with tufted, pinnately compound, finely dissected leaves arranged along the entire length of the submersed portion of the stem; leaves on the emergent portion simple, elliptic, sessile and coarsely serrate; flowers white, in terminal racemes in the axils of the upper leaves; petals 4; fruit a 1-chambered, globular pod (Lake Cress). Fig. 73 ....*Neobeckia* (*Armoracia*)

205b. Plants not as above....................................206

206a. Stems narrow, long, cordlike and lax, bearing alternate (or more often whorled), pinnately compound, feathery leaves with threadlike divisions; flowers small, inconspicuous, in whorls on

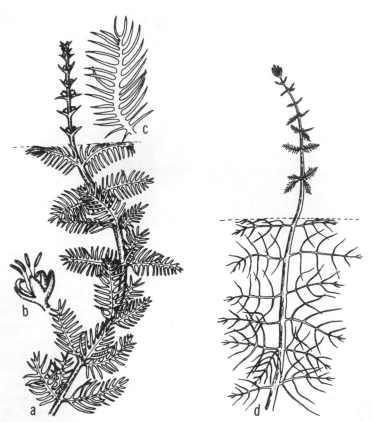

Fig. 117. *Myriophyllum* (Haloragaceae) a. *Myriophyllum exalbescens*, habit of plant; b. Flower; c. Leaf; d. *M. verticillatum*.

the upper part of the stem, the whorls subtended by bracts which are either simple or pinnately lobed; the flower-bearing portion of the stem emergent (Milfoil). Fig. 117..........*Myriophyllum*

Plants of this genus form dense, submersed beds. They are rooted but are often found floating freely. When mature the flowering apices of the stems appear above the water surface. The whorled leaves are finely dissected and pinnately compound. One species (*M. tenellum*) has reduced, knoblike leaves only. There are nine species widely distributed in the United States. They are useful in aeration and as food for muskrat and moose; seeds are eaten by many kinds of birds.

206b. Stems stout, the upper branches in a whorl and inflated, the lower undivided portion of the stem bearing pinnately compound leaves which are longer than in *Myriophyllum;* flowers small, consisting of a calyx with 5 lobes and a 5-lobed corolla that has a short tube; the fruit a 5-valved capsule; flowers arranged in whorls on the inflated branches; plants often floating, sometimes rooted on muddy shores (Featherfoil). Fig. 115..........*Hottonia*

209a. Leaves sessile, the leaf divided into threads from the point of origin on the stem; emersed leaves elliptic, pinnately lobed and coarsely serrate; infloresence a head in which there are both ray flowers (marginal) and tubular flowers (central) (Compositae, Water Marigold). Fig. 63.......................*Megalodonta*

209b. Leaves with a petiole, the divisions arising at the end of a short stalk; emersed leaves oval, floating leaves with peltate blades; flowers white or yellow with 3 petals and sepals, borne singly on peduncles in the axils of leaves (Fanwort; Parrot Feather). Fig. 33.....................................*Cabomba*

210a. (208) Leaves twice-divided, the primary divisions palmate, the secondary pinnately compound, usually alternate but sometimes opposite; stems hollow; flowers in umbels (Water Hemlock). Fig. 113...*Cicuta*

211a. Leaves pinnately or palmately compound, the leaflets elliptical, stalked, the margins coarsely serrate; lateral leaf veins straight to the margin; inflorescence a head (Compositae), terminal or axilary, the ray flowers sometimes wanting (Bur Marigold). Fig. 118 ....*Bidens*

Species of this genus live in wet meadows, marshes and swales; are somtimes marginal in shallow lake water. Some species occur in more arid situations. The composite type of inflorescence may or may not have ray flowers. The abundant fruits are used by many birds, both upland and aquatic. *Bidens* species are widely distributed in the United States.

211b. Leaves pinnately and deeply lobed so as to appear compound, the divisions narrow and with entire margins; flowers greenish-white, solitary or borne 2, 3 together in the axils of leaves; plants covered with sticky hairs. Fig. 42 ....*Leucospora*

212a. (207) Leaves dichotomously divided.......................213

Figure 118   Figure 119

Fig. 118.   *Bidens* (Compositae) Habit of plant.

Fig. 119.   *Ceratophylum* (Ceratophyllaceae)   a. Habit of *Ceratophyllum demersum;* b. Pistilate flower; c. Leaf.

This is the familiar Coon Tail, so-called because of the densely bushy stem tips. Plants are readily identified by the whorls of dichotomously forked leaves that have marginal teeth or horns. This is one of the few genera without roots. Plant stems may have a portion embedded in bottom sediments. The flowers and fruits are solitary in the axils of leaves, showing as small, red cylinders. *Ceratophyllum* is only moderately efficient as an aerator, but plants are much used by muskrats and by birds.

221a. Plants consisting of elongate, spatula-shaped lobes, arranged in a cross-shaped fashion, each lobe bearing a single root, plants floating in tangled clumps just below the water surface, or clustered about submersed aquatic plants (Star Duckweed). Fig. 4 .... *Lemna trisulca*

221b. Plants otherwise 222

222a. Plant consisting of one or more pairs of broadly oval to nearly circular leaves, attached to a short stem, the upper surface with stiff bristles; (a third submersed leaf arises from the ventral side of the stem at the same node as the one bearing the dorsal leaves, the ventral leaf highly dissected and root-like, chlorophylless, bears sporocarps when plants are mature); roots lacking (Water Fern; Floating Moss). Fig. 20 ...... *Salvinia*

222b. Plants consisting of several overlapping scalelike leaves which are usually red-tinged, the leaves possessing ventral lobes; leaves borne on a short, floating stem which has roots on the ventral surface (Water Velvet). Fig. 19 .... *Azolla*

223a. (217)—Plants attached, submersed, emergent, or on shore with minute, scalelike leaves or bracts, remote and not over-lapping on the stem 224

223b. Plants with leaves otherwise 225

224a. Plants with inflated, succulent leaves, either herbaceous or (as perennials) semi-woody at the base and shrublike; leaves minute, opposite scales; flowers small, borne in the axils of the upper scales and forming a terminal spike; plants of ocean beaches and alkali lake shores (Glasswort). Fig. 120 ... *Salicornia*

Species of this genus are low, sprawling plants with some erect stems. They inhabit salt-water or alkali beaches, occurring just above the high-tide level. The stems are succulent but the base of perennial species may be somewhat woody and tough. The leaves are opposite but are reduced to scales or "knobs," sometimes showing only as a rim at the node.

Fig. 120. *Salicornia* (Chenopodiaceae) Habit of plant.

224b. Erect, almost naked stems or flowering scapes from a subterranean branch, bearing a few, bilobed showy flowers; leaves
in the form of small scales which are united to form a tubelike
collar about the stem, or as alternately arranged 3-parted
bracts; (plants often have subterranean, colorless, club-shaped
leaves and modified branches bearing animal-trapping glands)
(Bladderwort). Fig. 116.............................*Utricularia*

225a. (223) Plants with small leaves reduced to rounded knoblike
members on upright stems, growing from submersed and subterranean, horizontal stems; flowers small and inconspicuous, in
the axils of upper leaves (Milfoil). Fig. 121....................
.....................................*Myriophyllum tenellum*

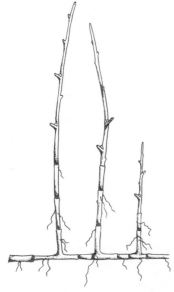

This is unlike other species in the
genus because the leaves occur as alternate, knoblike scales. This plant
grows on sandy shores or in shallow,
marginal water, the creeping branches
sending up naked stems.

Fig. 121. *Myriophyllum tenellum*
(Haloragidaceae) Habit of plant
showing knoblike leaves.

225b. Plants with green, narrow and linear, ovate or elliptic leaves,
numerous on the stem.................................226

226a. Small (a few mm long) green leaves, opposite on the stem..227

226b. Leaves alternate, usually crowded and overlapping........228

227a. Plants prostrate and matted, or partially erect, rooting at the nodes; leaves obovate or spatula-shaped, 3-5 mm long to as much as 1 cm (in some species), lying against the ground in terrestrial species; flowers solitary, sessile in the axils of leaves; sepals and petals 2 to 4, pistils 2 to 81; fruit a minute capsule with thin walls (Waterwort). Fig. 53......................*Elatine*

227b. Dwarf plants which are tufted and erect or sometimes creeping, rooted at the base of the stem; leaves narrow, elongate bracts; flowers solitary on a short peduncle, axial in the leaves; petals and sepals 3 or 4 and as many stamens; fruit a follicle (Pigmy Weed). Fig. 52...*Tillaea*

228a. (226) Leaves linear to filliform scales, alternate, with one vein, the apex of the leaf bidentate; stems prostrate and nearly covered by the overlapping leaves; flowers solitary in the axils of leaves; stamens and sepals 3, fruit a one-chambered capsule; plants floating or on shore (Pool Moss). Fig. 122........*Mayaca*

The densely branched stems have numerous, small, scalelike leaves. The plants form floating mats and although it is a flowering plant it is well-named Pool Moss. The small, white or pink flowers are solitary on slender peduncles. There are two species in southern states. They are undoubtedly efficient aerators but there is no known biological importance.

Fig. 122. *Mayaca* (Mayacaceae) a. Habit of plant; b. Fruit.

228b. Plants different; "leaves" oval, elliptic or nearly circular, often closely overlapping on procumbent, spreading "stems" (Mosses). 229

229a. "Leaves" with a midrib.................................230

229b. "Leaves" without a midrib, arranged in 3 rows, closely overlapping, often dark green or blackish, somewhat trough-shaped
or with a keel. Fig. 16.............................*Fontinalis*

230a. "Leaves" spirally arranged on an elongated, branched "stem,"
or in 2 rows, but spreading from all sides, sickle-shaped and
curling, the apex of the "stem" with a curling tuft. Fig. 18......
....*Drepanocladus*

230b. "Leaves" in 2 rows, spreading from 2 sides of the "stem," having
a superficial plate of cells forming a pocket along one side of
leaf at the base. Fig. 17.............................*Fissidens*

231a. (216) Leaves in the form of chlorophylless teeth in a whorl
at the nodes of branched, jointed green stems, the teeth black
or brown; stems otherwise leafless and bearing terminal sporangiophores arranged in a cone; the stem fluted and rough
to the touch because of silicon deposits (Horse Tail Fern). Fig. 123
....*Equisetum*

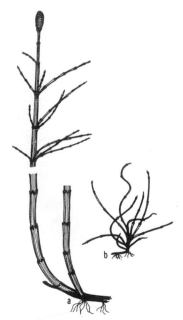

This is the familiar Horse Tail
genus of fernlike plants. A few
species are aquatic such as *E.
fluviatile* or semi-aquatic, as are
E. scirpoides, E. littorale and *E.
palustre*. Plants have green, jointed
and fluted stems which are leafless except for a whorl of chlorophylless scales at the joints. *E.
fluviatile* is important in filling in
of lakes. Dense meadows of the
plant may occur in lagoons and
bays. It is also important as food
for muskrats. Some birds use the
upper parts of the stems for grit
because of the large quantity of
silicon in the epidermal cell walls.
Because of their hard texture
Equisetum species have been used
as scouring rushes by Indians.

Fig. 123. *Equisetum* (Equisetaceae)
a. *Equisetum fluviatile*; b. *E. scirpoides*.

231b. Leaves club-shaped or spatula-shaped, on horizontal stems which
may also bear modified branches that have animal-trapping
glands; vertical branches bearing terminal flowers, the scape
naked but with a few alternate or opposite scales (Bladderwort).
Fig. 116 . . . . *Utricularia* (p.p.)

232a. (36) Plants with long, tapering, grasslike leaves with subparallel
margins, clasping the stem, the blade bearing a liplike ligule
at the base where the leaf forms its sheath (See *Triglochin,*
Fig. 144 in the Juncaginaceae, however); leaves 2-ranked; stems
hollow, round in cross section; flowers in spikelets* which are
composed of 2 glumes (basal scales) above which are 1 or
several florets, each floret composed of a lemma, a palea,
a pistil and stamens (in rare instances flowers are monoecious,
Zizania, e.g.; or dioecious as in some none-aquatic genera)
(Grass Famiy, Gramineae) (see text figure 1) 233

232b. Plants otherwise; leaves without ligules 240

233a. Flowers in terminal panicles with those in the upper part
pistillate, the spikelets closely arranged, those below staminate
and more loosely arranged; (plants often submersed when young,
the leaf blades floating on the surface) (Wild Rice; Indian Rice).
Fig. 124 . . . . *Zizania*

This is a tall, aquatic grass of sloughs and lagoons which, because
of its abundant, edible seed has been important in the economy and
social life of Indian tribes. Seeds are harvested and sold commercially
in Michigan, Wisconsin and Minnesota. The grains are highly useful
to birds as food, and the dense stands make suitable nesting sites.
Another species, *Z. texana* is rare, occurring only in Texas.

233b. Flowers with stamens and pistils in the same spikelet 234

---

*See *Glyceria borealis* and *G. fluitans* (Fig. 127, submersed grasses, with ribbonlike
leaves, which seldom flower except when emergent.)

234a. Flowers in plumelike panicles which persist as feathery white tufts throughout the winter; plants canelike up to 4 M tall; leaves relatively broad and widely spreading from the stem; plants usually growing in dense stands in lake margins or in sloughs, wet ditches, etc. (Cane Grass). Fig. 125..............*Phragmites*

This tall, cane grass forms dense stands in quiet water of lake bays, in sloughs and in roadside ditches. It is important biologically as cover for birds and other small animals. The leaves are wide, up to 5 cm in large specimens. The stems bear dense panicles of flowers, the scales purple at first, but the numerous silky hairs of the spikelets produce conspicuous white plumes which persist throughout the winter months. The one species (and its varieties) is widely distributed over the United States.

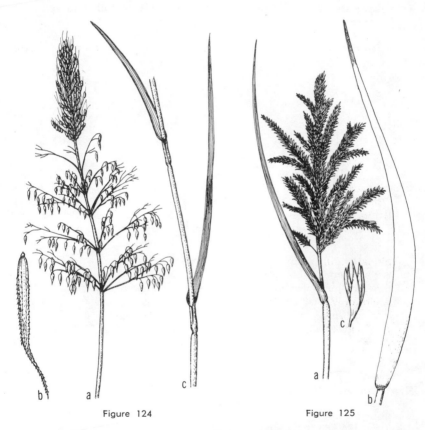

Figure 124   Figure 125

Fig. 124. *Zizania aquatica* (Gramineae) a. Panicle of staminate (above) and pistillate (below) flowers; b. Achene; c. Stem and leaves.

Fig. 125. *Phragmites maximus* (Gramineae) a. Panicle; b. Leaf; c. Floret.

117

234b. Plants otherwise; shorter leaves; plants not so tall (up to 1½ M); inflorescence not plumelike................................235

235a. Spikelet forming oval (but compressed) clumps on short lateral stalks, the clumps forming several rows and overlapping so as to form a rather compact panicle; spikelets arranged on more than one side, without spines; plants with many leaves, up to 1.5 M tall (Canary Reed Grass). Fig. 126........*Phalaris*

This species occurs in dense clumps, with the flowering stems rising well above the leaves. Plants may be up to 1½ M tall. The spikelets

Figure 126   Figure 127

Fig. 126. *Phalaris arundinacea* (Gramineae) a. Habit of plant; b. Panicle; c. Lemma; d. Stem and leaf.

Fig. 127. *Glyceria* (Gramineae) a. *Glyceria fluitans*, habit in submersed position; b. Panicle; c. Lemma; d. Spikelet; e. Stem and leaves.

are clumped and closely appressed so that a relatively firm, cylindrical inflorescence is produced. The leaves are relatively wide, up to 15 mm. Seeds are much used by birds. The species occurs throughout the United States, both in marginal aquatic and in dry situations.

236a. Plants with erect stems growing from rhizomes; panicle usually loose and spreading, the spikelets sessile, compact or loose, with several flowers; the spikelets elliptic or ovate, not compressed; lemma ridged with 5 to 9 nerves; glumes unequal in length, shorter than the first lemma; leaf margins joined at the base to form a closed sheath; plants of marshes, forming dense meadows, or submersed with the long, narrow leaves (reddish) floating at the surface (submersed plants not flowering) (Manna Grass). Fig. 127..*Glyceria*

This genus includes several species which are either aquatic or semi-aquatic, forming dense meadows and providing much food and cover for birds. Several species have spreading, loose panicles. *Glyceria fluitans* and *G. borealis* commonly grow submersed; have narrow, ribbonlike leaves floating out on the surface. These species seem never to produce flowers when submersed. The genus is distinctive in having a closed sheath (usually) at the base of the blade.

236b. Plants otherwise; panicle different; stems from rhizomes or not
....237

237a. Spikelets overlapping, all on one side....................238

237b. Spikelets otherwise, compactly arranged in a cylindrical spike; glumes blunt-pointed but fringed dorsally; young spikes showing stamens conspicuously (Fox Tail Grass). Fig. 128.. *Alopecurus*
Species of this genus form rather sparse patches on the margins of lakes and in shallow water. They are relatively short, usually 2 or 3 dm tall. Spikes of flowers are dense, forming an inflorescence much like that of Timothy. The stamens are long and conspicuous, showing red and yellow in the spikelet. *Alopecurus aequalis* is the most common and widely distributed; is useful as a soil binder.

238a. Spikelets with a fringed margin, overlapping, in one row (Cut Grass). Fig. 129...................................... *Leersia*
This genus has overlapping spikelets and in one row, giving a characteristic, one-sided appearance to the branches of the panicles.

Figure 128   Figure 129

Fig. 128. *Alopecurus* (Gramineae) a. Habit of plant; b. Lemma and awn.
Fig. 129. *Leersia* (Gramineae) Habit of plant.

Two species and their varieties are widely distributed on lake margins and in wet meadows. Plants and seeds are used by both birds and muskrats.

238b. Spikelets in 2 rows....................................239

239a. Spikelets about as long as wide, in one-sided spikes that are about 3 times as long as wide (Slough Grass). Fig. 130........
....*Beckmannia*
    In this genus the spikelets form two rows on one side of the stem. The panicle is not open and loose but rather close, and is interrupted

Figure 130   Figure 131

Fig. 130. *Beckmannia* (Gramineae) Habit of plant.
Fig. 131. *Spartina pectinata* (Gramineae) Habit of plant.

121

rather than continuous. *B. syzigachni* is found in suitable habitats throughout the United States, although apparently it does not occur in the Gulf region.

239b. Spikelets elongate, the palea often tapering to a long point; spikes up to 12 times the width in length; plants tall, up to 1.5-2 M with many leaves that taper to narrowed apices, long and whiplike (Cord Grass). Fig. 131 . . . . *Spartina*

This species of the genus grows rankly in sloughs, salt marshes and along beach margins. Plants may be as much as 2 M tall. The leaves are very long, coarse and rough, have a whiplike tip. The spike-lets are compressed laterally and arranged in one-sided spikes which are erect. Other species are found in coastal marshs. All are important in erosion control and in soil-building, partly because the plants have large, cordlike rhizomes.

240a. (232) Plants with long, slender green stems, more than 10 times their diameter; leaves lacking or occurring as sheaths at the base of the stem 241

240b. Plants with elongate leaves, either grasslike, ribbonlike, linear, linear-oblong to linear lanceolate 244

241a. Leaves on the stem reduced, without blades, occurring as hollow petioles with basal leaves pinnately compound and with long petioles, the leaflets nearly circular or broadly ovate; flowers small, white, in an umbel (Dropwort). Fig. 110 . . . *Oxypolis*

241b. Plants otherwise 242

242a. Leaves consisting of a sheath at the base of the slender stem (with or without a continuing tonguelike blade), or with a bladelike involucre at the base of the flower spikelets, the involucre continuing and appearing as an extension of the stem;

flowers borne in overlapping scales, consisting of 1 pistil and
1 to 3 stamens (Bulrush). Fig. 132..................Scirpus (p.p.)

This genus contains both emergent species (sometimes growing in
water 3 M in depth) or marginal and shore forms. Included are the
common Bulrushes that have many economic importances (boat-build-
ing, baskets, mats, etc.). *Scirpus validus* grows to a height of 15 or
20 feet. *S. americanus* often forms dense stands on beaches and in
shallow water. Species like *S. atrovirens* or *S. atrocinctus* form stands
in swales and ditches. *S. subterminalis* grows submersed and forms
dense meadows of grasslike plants with the stem and leaves lax and
floating. Stems of *Scirpus* are either triangular or round in cross section.
The inflorescence of spikelets is subterminal with subtending involucral

Fig. 132. *Scirpus* (Cyperaceae) a. *Scirpus validus*, habit, showing swollen stem base; b. *S. americanus*, habit showing triangular
stem; c. Nutlet; d. *S. atrovirens*, habit; e. Spikelet; f. Nutlet.

leaves (grasslike in *S. atrovirens,* e.g.) which may be round in cross section and extend beyond the inflorescence so as to appear like a continuation of the stem. Species have many biological importances, as food for muskrats, nesting sites for birds, as soilbinders and in the ageing of lakes.

243a. Leaves occurring as basal sheaths (which are open), without any tonguelike or bladelike extensions, and with a stemlike extension of the involucre which often appears as an elongation of the stem beyond the cluster of brown flowers, the flowers thus appearing to be lateral near the top of the stem; flowers with 3 sepals and petals, and with 3 or 6 stamens, the flowers appearing as small, brown lilylike blooms; capsule with many seeds (Rush). Fig. 133...............................*Juncus**

Species of this genus are often clumped, with several to many culms in each plant. There are two principal expressions; one being a naked stem with a sheath at the base. Another form is a leaf-bearing stem with flat blades. The leafless stems have a cluster of flowers near the tip, and extending from its base a round leaf which appears as a continuation of the stem. The sheath at the base may or may not have a flat blade extending from the margin. The thickened plant bases are used by muskrats for food, and the seeds are used by upland birds.

243b. Leaves occurring only as a collarlike sheath at the base of the stem; spikelets terminal on elongate, naked stems which may be angular (*E. Robbinsii*) or round in cross section; pistil with a persistent style which enlarges to form a tubercle at the summit of the nutlet (Spike Rush). Fig. 134...........*Eleocharis*

There are many aquatic and semi-aquatic species in this genus, growing submersed, emergent, and marginal. Some are important in succession as ponds age and disappear. The plants are distinctive in having a solitary spike at the apex of a naked culm, hence the name of Spike Rush. Some species are short and form a turf on lake bottoms, in shallow water, or on muddy shores. Others are tall, clumped and tufted, as much as 4 dm high. These plants are important as soil binders, and as food for birds. Muskrats also are known to use these plants as food.

Luzula, a related genus of semi-aquatic habitats has closed sheaths and a capsule-like fruit which has 3 seeds.

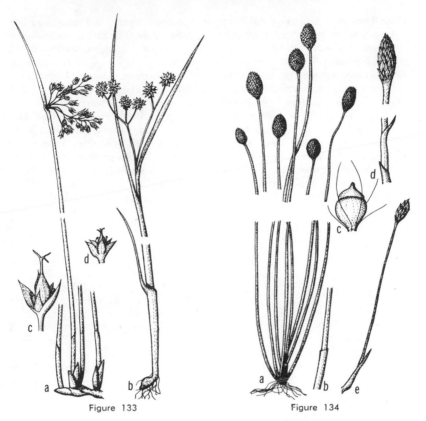

Figure 133   Figure 134

Fig. 133. *Juncus* (Juncaceae) a. *Juncus effusus*, habit of plant portion; b. *J. nodosus;* c. Flower of *J. effusus;* d. Flower of *J. nodosus.*

Fig. 134. *Eleocharis* (Cyperaceae) a. *Eleocharis obtusa*, habit of plant; b. Sheath at base of culm; c. Nutlet; d. *E. palustris*, lower part of stem and terminal head of flowers; e. *E. albida*, habit of a flowering shoot.

248a. Leaves somewhat rubbery or leathery; vein not showing, or scarcely so; stem branched; leaves often basal but sometimes on the stem also; flowers solitary, arising from a spathe (Mud Plantain). Fig. 94 . . . .*Heteranthera*

248b. Plants otherwise; not branched; leaves mostly basal (sometimes a few on the stem); veins apparent 249

249a. Leaves clustered, ribbonlike, up to 3 feet long; all from a subterranean rootstock, showing a prominent midvein (See Fig. 135-d), and several lateral parallel nerves, with a marginal zone in which there are only a few cross veinlets, thus forming a distinct border; flowers of two sorts; pistillate solitary on a long, slender scape, the bloom floating at the surface; staminate flowers on a basal spathe; plants mostly of deep water (Water Celery). Fig. 135 . . . .*Vallisneria*

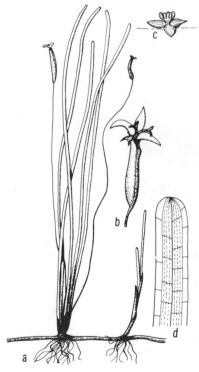

The long, ribbonlike leaves arise vertically, but lax, in tufts from a creeping rootstock. Sometimes the leaves are a full meter in length. Plants may form veritable "forests" in quiet water and provide suitable cover for small fish. Muskrats, fish and birds use *Vallisneria* for food. Pistillate flowers float at the surface on a long, spiral thread from the bottom, whereas staminate flowers are in stalked spathes in the axils of the leaves. These break loose and float to the surface at maturity. *Vallisneria* is often planted in fish nurse ponds (as Water Celery). This is a species which is widely distributed throughout the United States wherever there are suitable habitats. *V. neotropicalis* grows in subtropical United States.

Fig. 135. *Vallisneria americana* (Hydrocharitaceae) a. Habit of plant with pistillate flowers; b. Pistillate flower and spathe; c. Staminate flower floating at surface after release from base of plant; d. Leaf tip.

249b. Plants otherwise; leaves differently veined.................250

250a. Leaves clustered, mostly basal, long lax, ribbonlike (often floating at the surface), usually bluntly pointed but acute in some
forms, without prominent longitudinal veins, the cross and longitudinal veinlets forming a meshwork of rectangular, cubical
spaces; flowers in heads, monoecious, the lower pistillate and
the upper staminate, the heads beadlike in arrangement in the
upper part of the stem; perianth consisting of scales (Bur Reed).
Fig. 136...*Sparganium*

Fig. 136. *Sparganium* (Sparganiaceae) a. *Sparganium chlorocarpum* type,
habit showing base of leaves and inflorescence at apex of plant; b. Fruit;
c. Cross section of leaf (diagram); d. *S. androcladum* type, base of plant; e.
Inflorescence; f. Section of leaf to show venation; g. Flower; h. Nutlet; i. Tips
of leaves.

Most species are found emergent in lake margins and sloughs, but some (*Sparganium fluctuans*) are submersed in deep ponds, the ribbon-like leaves floating at the surface. Emergent leaves are trough-shaped or keeled on the back in the basal portion. Burlike heads of fruits may be as much as 5 cm in diameter and are used by wildfowl whereas muskrats devour the entire plant.

250b. **Leaves ribbonlike but very narrow (2 to 10 mm wide); clustered, erect, but lax and often floating at the surface; with one prominent midvein and several, indistinct parallel nerves, the cross veinlets forming a pattern of larger elongate, rectangular spaces; perianth or 3 green sepals and 3 white petals; flowers in whorls on a long, naked scape; some flowers with either stamens or pistils only (Arrowhead; Delta Potato). Fig. 92......** ....*Sagittaria*

251a. **(247) Leaves dark green, stiff, awllike but somewhat flattened, in general filiform, with a broad sheath at the base, blades up to 3 mm wide in the midregion; flowers monoecious, the carpellate in pairs; the staminate solitary on a naked, erect scape. Fig. 137..*Littorella***

This is a small plant, with leaves up to 7 cm long, growing submersed in northern states. In the vegetative condition it is difficult to differentiate these small plants from *Ruppia* and from *Ranunculus reptans*. Plants are monoecious, the staminate being on a scape whereas the pistillate are at the base of the scape. No biological importance is attached to this species.

Fig. 137. *Littorella americana* (Plantaginaceae) a. Habit of plant; b. Pistillate flower.

251b. Leaves not dark green, but awllike, somewhat flattened, up to 3 cm long, not sheathing at the base; inflorescence a scape with a few small, white flowers in a raceme; 4 petals and sepals; plants of shallow water (Awlwort). Fig. 138 . . . . *Subularia*

The linear, basal leaves forming a rosette are much unlike other members of the mustard family. The flowering scape with white flowers may be as much as 10 cm high. *S. aquatica* is rare but occurs in both Atlantic and Pacific states. As far as is known *Subularia* has no biological importances.

Fig. 138. *Subularia aquatica* (Cruciferae) Habit.

252a. (246) Leaves flat, 2-ranked, swordlike, equitant-sheathing at the base; inflorescence a spadix of numerous, closely arranged flowers composed of 6 yellowish bracts, 6 stamens and a pistil; the spadix cylindrical and borne on a scape with a spathe continuing beyond the spadix as an extension of the scape; plants spicy aromatic (Sweet Flag). Fig. 139 . . . . *Acorus*

The sheathing, narrow but swordlike leaves of *Acorus* superficially resemble young *Typha* plants. They may be as much as one M in height, growing among cattail in the margins of lakes and in lagoons and marshes. The thick rhizomes are much used by muskrats for food. The spicy aroma from crushed leaves explains the common name of Sweet Flag. Records show that *Acorus* is absent from southwest and southeastern United States.

252b. Plants otherwise; leaves not equitant 253

253a. Leaves grasslike, mostly basal, but some cauline; flowers in spikelets that are closely arranged to form a head or umbel, with one or more leaf-like bracts below the head, the inflorescence a long shoot that is almost naked, sometimes with a few bractlike leaves; bristles of flowers long, becoming white and forming "cotton balls" (Cotton Grass). Fig. 140. . Eriophorum

Species grow mostly in Sphagnum bogs where they are showy as Cotton Grass. In the tundras of the Arctic conspicuous white stands are produced. The "cotton" appearance is a result of the long, fine bristles of the inflorescence scales, the spikelets forming a dense terminal head. It is not known that Eriophorum has any biological importances.

Figure 139   Figure 140

Fig. 139. Acorus calamus (Araceae) a. Habit of plant; b. Spadix.
Fig. 140. Eriophorum (Cyperaceae) a. Habit of plant; b. Scale with bristles.

253b. Plants otherwise; inflorescence not forming a cotton ball.....254

254a. Plants with a stout rhizome, giving rise to long, slender scapes bearing spikelets of flowers subterminally, and with a tuft of long slender leaves at the base; plants submersed (Bulrush). Fig. 141................................*Scirpus subterminalis*

This species has long, lax leaves from the base, the plant growing submersed and often forming dense "meadows." The leaves and the flowering stem float at the surface of the water. The inflorescence has but one spikelet. The species is important in both fishery and aquatic bird biology.

254b. Plants otherwise...255

255a. Leaves grasslike, sometimes broad and inflated, sheathed for as much as one-half their length; inflorescence a long, slender scape with a round head of imbricated scales, yellowish flowers in their axils (Yellow-eyed Grass). Fig. 142..............*Xyris*

The Yellow-eyed Grasses grow on beaches or in wet meadows, and occasionally in water at lake margins. In general they may be used as an index of acid situations. The long, narrow leaves are flat and are sheathed for as much as one-half their length. The small flowers occur in globular or oval heads at the end of naked scapes and are in the axils of bracts. It is claimed that mallard ducks use *Xyris* for food.

255b. Leaves not sheathed as above; inflorescence not a head on a naked scape...256

256a. Leaves with a broad, membranous sheath that bears a pair of ligulelike lobes at the upper margin; inflorescence a long, slender spike with numerous, small 3-merous flowers (Arrow Grass). Fig. 143...*Triglochin*

This species occurs as a clump of long, slender, basal leaves and a spike of small, green, lilylike flowers. *T. maritima* is the most common species of the genus, occurring in salt and alkaline marshes or basic soils. There appears to be no biological importance.

Figure 141   Figure 142   Figure 143

Fig. 141. *Scirpus subterminalis* (Cyperaceae) Habit of plant.

Fig. 142. *Xyris torta* (Xyridaceae) Habit.

Fig. 143. *Triglochin maritima* (Juncaginaceae) a. Habit of plant; b. Capsule.

256b. **Leaves without a basal sheath that bears ligules**..........257

257a. **Leaves sheathing at the base, from a slender rootstock; inflorescence a head or short raceme on a long, slender, naked scape that is dotted with sticky glands (False Asphodel). Fig. 144**
....*Tofieldia*

This is an herb with 3-parted, yellow flowers, many in a head at the apex of a naked scape. The leaves are elongate-linear and remindful of *Triglochin*. The species is found in bogs and wet meadows, especially at higher altitudes.

257b. **Plants otherwise; without sticky glands on the flowering scape.**
....258

258a. **Leaves long and slender, more or less erect, up to 1 M long; flowers showy, blue or pink, in an umbel (Flowering Rush). Fig. 145**...*Butomus*

This is a tall, showy plant with a naked scape bearing an umbel of blue flowers (or pinkish). There is a tuft of linear, basal leaves nearly as long as the flowering shoot which may be 1 M tall. The leaves are sheathing and keeled in the basal section. *Butomus* is limited in distribution to northern United States, but has been transplanted to various parts of the country by sportsmen clubs since it is useful as wildfowl food.

258b. Leaves shorter; inflorescence otherwise.....................259

259a. Leaves up to 10 cm long, broad at the base from a padlike stem, rather rigid; inflorescence a compact head, the intervening bracts white-tipped and giving a woolly appearance; roots white and showing septations (Pipewort). Fig. 146..........*Eriocaulon*

Figure 144   Figure 145   Figure 146

Fig. 144. *Tofieldia glutinosa* (Liliaceae) Habit of plant.

Fig. 145. *Butomus umbellatus* (Butomaceae) Habit of plant.

Fig. 146. *Eriocaulon septangulare* (Eriocaulaceae) a. Habit of plant; b. Head of flowers; c. Single flower.

There are several species of *Eriocaulon* which are limited in their distribution. They occur as linear-leaved, tufted plants. The elongate leaves are either flat or concave, shorter than the long, naked scape which bears a spherical head of small flowers that are whitish and wooly. Plants are indices of sandy, acid soil and are commonly found in marshes and on grassy beaches, *E. septangulare* is widely distributed in midwest and northern United States.

259b. Leaves mostly shorter; inflorescence otherwise.............260

260a. Plants essentially without a stem; leaves clustered, broad at the base and imbricate, often awl-shaped but sometimes flattened; flowers small, white, 2 or 3 in a raceme that usually exceeds the length of the leaves (Awlwort). Fig. 138...*Subularia*

260b. Plants with creeping stems; leaves tufted but filiform throughout their length, not imbricate at the base; flowers small (3 mm wide), white or purple, solitary on a slender, naked, recurved stalk; flowers 5-parted (Mudwort). Fig. 98...........*Limosella*

261a. (245) Leaves hollow and tubular, in a rosette from a padlike stem, broadened at the base to enclose a sporangium; the stem bearing a mass of short roots (Quillwort Fern). Fig. 147...
....*Isoetes*

This fern appears as a clump of bunchgrass, either submersed or in wet meadows. Some species have leaves nearly 1 M tall. The hollow leaves from a padlike stem have a sporangium at the base on the inner (adaxial) face when mature. Some species constitute an index for soft-water or acid habitats where they sometimes form a veritable meadows over lake bottoms. The plants are used as food by some diving birds, by deer and by muskrats.

Fig. 147. *Isoetes* (Isoetaceae) a. Habit of plant; b. Base of leaf showing sporangium.

261b. Leaves not hollow; not bearing sporangia................262

262a. Plants dwarfed (3 to 6 cm tall, rarely up to 10 cm), prostrate with creeping stem, sometimes a threadlike rootstocks from which tufted leaves arise......................................263

262b. Plants larger, leaves up to 6 dm tall; flowering scapes up to 12 dm tall; with thick rootstocks, or pads; leaves mostly in rosettes...266

263a. Leaves slender, 2 to 4 cm long (up to 5 cm), in clumps of 2 or 3 (sometimes only 1) from each node of a prostrate, threadlike stem; plants forming dense mats (submersed or on shores); flowers yellow, solitary at the nodes (Buttercup; Water Spearwort). Fig. 148...........................*Ranunculus reptans*

This species of water buttercup is unlike others in the genus in having tufted, linear or spatulate leaves on creeping stems. From the nodes solitary flowers on relatively long peduncles arise. This species is found on muddy shores.

Fig. 148. *Ranunculus reptans* (Ranunculaceae) Habit of plant.

263b. Plants otherwise, mostly larger; leaves 6 cm tall, rarely up to 10 cm...264

264a. Leaves dark green, rather stiff, filiform (but somewhat flattened), up to 3 mm wide in the midregion, with a broad sheathed base; flowers on a slender, erect scape, monoecious, the carpellate in pairs, the staminate solitary. Fig. 137..............*Littorella*

264b. Plants otherwise; leaves without a broad sheath at the base..265

135

265a. Leaves mostly basal but sometimes alternate on the stem; stipules fused at base of leaves; flowers minute, in an umbel on a scape that is borne on an erect shoot and sheathed by a leaf base; flowers simple, consisting of 2 sessile stamens and 4 sessile pistils (Widgeon Grass). Fig. 149..............Ruppia

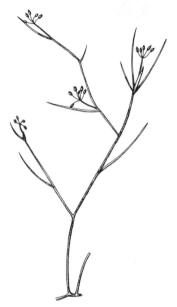

This plant has slender, grasslike leaves which are broader at the base and sheathing, arising from prostrate runners. A short or long flowering scape arises from the same node as the leaves. Ruppia is found throughout the United States on saline or alkaline shores. The fruits are much used by aquatic birds.

Fig. 149. *Ruppia maritima* (Naidaceae) Habit of plant.

265b. Leaves in tufts of from 5 to 10 on threadlike runners; flowers perfect, 3 mm wide, white or purple, solitary on a recurved peduncle from the stem node (Mudwort). Fig. 98.......Limosella

266a. (262) Plants with long, terete leaves, up to 6 dm tall; scapes 12 dm, sheathed at the base and arising from a short rhizome which is covered with white leaf bases of old leaves, the sheath with a ligule; inflorescence a crowded, spikelike raceme (Arrow Grass). Fig. 143.............................Triglochin

266b. Plants smaller; inflorescence not a spike...................267

267a. Plants stemless; leaves short, 3 cm tall, awllike, in a tuft; inflorescence a scape with a few small, white flowers in a raceme; several scapes arising from each leaf tuft; flowers with 4 petals and sepals (Awlwort). Fig. 138..........Subularia

267b. Plants otherwise; leaves longer...........................268

268a. Plants with leaves to 60 cm (usually about 35 cm), not translucent; sheathing for as much as one-half their length; inflorescence an ovate spike, with perfect and imperfect flowers intermixed, consisting of a sessile stamen and a single carpel, or at times with 2 basal pistillate flowers in leaf axes (Flowering Quillwort). Fig. 150...*Lilaea*

This species has linear, ribbonlike leaves, sheathing at the base, which may be up to 60 cm tall. Each plant has several naked stalks bearing a cone-shaped spike of flowers. Also some flowers are borne low in the axils of the leaves. *L. subulata* is found on alkaline flats, tidal basins and on deltas of rivers. No biological importance is known.

Fig. 150. *Lilaea subulata* (Juncaginaceae) a. Habit; b. Basal achene (stylized).

268b. Plant with leaves 2 to 8 cm long, in a basal rosette, translucent when held to the light and showing cross markings; roots white with cross markings; inflorescence a naked stalk, bearing a head of white flowers and bracts which are intermingled, the bracts whitish so that a white head is produced; flowers either pistillate or staminate (Pipewort). Fig. 146...........*Eriocaulon*

271a. Leaves filiform and tapering to a point....................272

271b. Leaves flat, rounded at the apex........................273

272a. Leaves abruptly broadened at the base, margins with various forms of sharp serrations; leaves linear, up to 8 times the diameter in length, mostly crowded, bunched or whorled, sometimes opposite; flowers solitary in the axils of the leaves (Bushy Pondweed). Fig. 151.....................................*Naias*

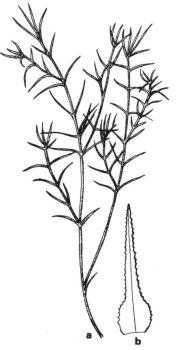

This genus is entirely aquatic and submersed, forming bushy growths which may be scattered or in extensive patches. The leaves are linear and have specifically characteristic toothed margins and base shapes. *N. flexilis* is the most common and widely distributed species. It is excellent as an aerator, and the seeds, although scant, are much used by birds for food.

a   b

Fig. 151. *Naias flexilis* (Naidaceae) a. Habit; b. Leaf showing characteristic base.

272b. Leaves threadlike, filiform, narrowed symmetrically from the base to a fine point, 0.5 mm wide, no serrations on the margins; (leaves sometimes whorled as well as opposite); flowers 2 to 5 in the axils of leaves; plants perennial with a slender rhizome (Horned Pondweed). Fig. 152............*Zannichellia*

Leaves are linear and opposite and rather sparse as compared with *Naias*. Like that genus the sessile, monoecious flowers and fruits are borne in the axils of leaves. The flowers, without a calyx or corolla, are borne in a transparent spathe. The fruits are characteristic, being an elongate nutlet with a toothed, longitudinal ridge and an apical beak. *Z. palustris* is widely distributed over the United States in hard water and saline situations. Both the plants and the fruits are used by many birds for food.

273a. (271) Leaves narrow ribbons, indented at the apex, margins parallel (becoming spatulate to obovate in the upper part of the stem), forming a rosette at the apex of the stem; plants monoecious, stems unbranched (Water Starwort). Fig. 47 . . . . *Callitriche*

273b. Leaves narrow and not widened at the base, the same shape throughout the length of the stem; flowers perfect; stems branched (Water Purslane). Fig. 153 . . . . *Didiplis*

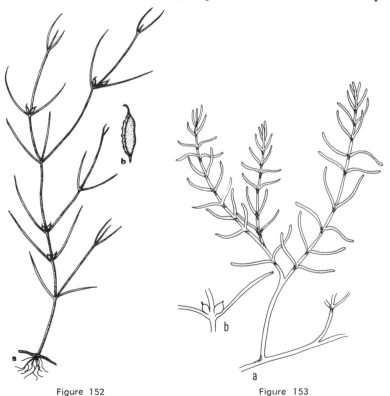

Figure 152   Figure 153

Fig. 152. *Zannichellia palustris* (Naidaceae) a. Habit; b. Fruit.

Fig. 153. *Didiplis* (Lythraceae) a. Habit of *Didiplis linearis*; b. Location of fruits.

Some species of *Didiplis* are strictly aquatic (*D. linearis, D. diandra*), or they may occur in the shallow water of lakes and continuing onto the shore mud. They are found mostly in eastern United States. The plants are dwarfish; have narrow, opposite leaves, although some varieties of the species have elongate-oval leaves (*D. diandra* especially). The flowers are small, greenish and are borne in the axils of the leaves. *Peplis diandra* is a synonym of the latter species name.

274a. (270) **Leaves elongate-ellipsoid, long-tapering at the base; flowers purple, in a dense cluster on a stalk arising in the axils of the leaves (Water Willow). Fig. 55** . . . . *Dianthera (Justicia)*

274b. Plants otherwise 275

275a. Leaves thin, oblong to linear, without a long-tapering base; flowers solitary, sessile or nearly so in the axils of leaves (Sea Milkwort). Fig. 25 . . . .*Glaux*

275b. Plants otherwise 276

276a. Leaves oblong-lanceolate, broad at the base and lobed, tapering to a sharp point; flowers sessile or on very short stalks. Fig. 154 . . . .*Ammannia*

The clasping leaves of this species are lanceolate, with one or two flowers in the axils. The plants are erect, growing on lake margins and in marshes. The stems are square in cross section. There are three semi-aquatic species in the genus, distributed in eastern and southern United States, *A. auriculata* being the most common.

276b. Plants otherwise 277

277a. Leaves linear, fleshy or succulent, with scalelike stipules, nearly round in cross section; leaves often fascicled although sometimes opposite; flowers pink or white, in terminal racemes (Sand Spurry). Fig. 155 . . . .*Spergularia*

This plant sprawls on tidal flats and on saline beaches. They are relatively small; have linear, opposite leaves which are nearly round in cross section. The small 5-merous flowers are solitary in the axils of leaves. This species occurs on both Atlantic and Pacific coasts in northern sections.

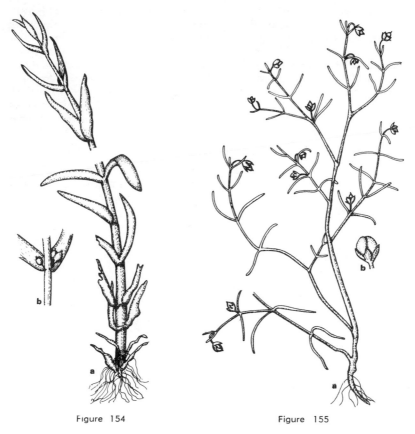

Figure 154   Figure 155

Fig. 154. *Ammannia auriculata* (Lythraceae) a. Habit; b. Fruits.
Fig. 155. *Spergularia canadensis* (Caryophyllaceae) a. Habit; b. Capsule.

277b. Leaves not fleshy, narrow but flat, elongate-elliptic with narrowed bases and a short petiole; flowers solitary in the axils
of leaves (Tooth-cup). Fig. 54.........................*Rotala*

278a. (269) Leaves whorled or bunched.......................279

278b. Leaves alternate.......................................281

141

279a. **Leaves grasslike, mostly alternate, but the involucral leaves sometimes whorled (Sedge). Fig. 156.................Cyperus**
This is a sedge with a solid, angular stem (in cross section) that has an inflorescence in which the scales are arranged in two rows. The spikelet of flowers accordingly is flattened, giving species in this genus a distinct appearance when in flower. *C. esculenta* (chufa) is a common beach species on which root tubers are formed (Ground Almonds) that are much-used by aquatic birds for food. Some species grow in shallow water, but mostly these are plants of grassy margins, wet meadows and ditches.

279b. **Leaves not grasslike in shape............................280**

280a. **Plants bushy with branched stems; leaves tufted or whorled, filiform with an abruptly widened base, the margins toothed; (leaves occasionally opposite) (Bushy Pondweed). Fig. 151..Naias**

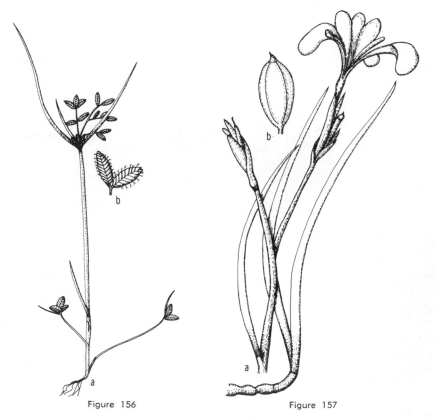

Figure 156   Figure 157

Fig. 156. *Cyperus* sp. (Cyperaceae) a. Habit; b. Spikelet.
Fig. 157. *Iris* (Iridaceae) a. Habit; b. Capsule.

280b. Plants without leaves tufted but in distinct whorls, as many as 12 at the node of an unbranched stem; submersed leaves longer (12 times longer than wide) and more lax than the leaves on the emergent section of the stem; flowers solitary, sessile, in the axils of leaves (Water Mare's Trail). Fig. 41........*Hippuris*

281a. (278) Leaves swordlike, sheathing blades, equitant, partly or mostly basal, from a thick rootstock (Flag). Fig. 157........*Iris*

The flag with its flat, sheathing swordlike leaves in clearly recognized, even when not in bloom. At least seven species occur in marshes and swamps. The most common is *I. versicolor* with blue flowers. *I. fulva* and *I. pseudacorus* are yellow or copper-colored. Muskrats are known to use the rootstocks for food.

281b. Leaves not flat and swordlike, and not equitant.............282

282a. Leaves filiform, dichotomously forked (Riverweed). Fig. 107....
....*Podostemum*

282b. Plants otherwise.......................................283

283a. Leaves short-filiform, not divided, simple, mostly basal but a few alternate on the stem, occurring in tufts from a horizontal runner; flowers in a simple umbel on a long or short stalk Widgeon Grass). Fig. 149.............................*Ruppia*

283b. Plants otherwise......................................284

284a. Plants with long-filiform leaves, threadlike from 0.1 to 3.0 mm wide, leaves with stipules (Pondweed). Fig. 46.....*Potamogeton*

284b. Plants otherwise...285

285a. Leaves long (½ to 2 M) and ribbonlike, flat or keeled at the back, the margins parallel; leaves lax when in water, or relatively rigid and erect when emergent......................286

285b. Leaves shorter, up to 1½ dm long, grasslike or linear, tapering gradually to a point.......................................289

286a. Plants of marine and brackish waters....................287

286b. Plants of fresh water or terrestrial.......................288

287a. Leaves up to 2 M long, slender, up to 6 mm wide, somewhat flattened to nearly terete, the leaf tip truncate or notched, the leaves arising from a stout, much-branched rhizome and sheathed at the base; flowers in a spadix which is enclosed by a spathe, the flowers in 2 rows on one side of the spike; carpellate flower with an obovate or cordate pistil, a short style and divergent stigma; plants dioecious (Surf Grass). Fig. 158.....*Phyllospadix*

There are two species of this genus in the shore waters of the Pacific. They are found in tide pools or on wave-swept rocks. The plants are similar to *Zostera* but differ in being dioecious and having a different type of rhizome. The plants are important as substrates for algae and small animals in marine biology.

287b. Leaves up to 1½ M long, wider than above (up to 12 mm at the base), rising from a slender roostock, bluntly rounded at the apex; erect stem leafy; plants monoecious; inflorescence a spadix, with two sorts of flowers alternate in 2 rows along the

144

axis; the carpellate flowers with a broadly ovoid ovary that has a long style and an erect stigma (Eel Grass). Fig. 159.... *Zostera*
This is the widely distributed and familiar Eel Grass, abundant in certain sections all along both the Pacific and Atlantic coasts of the United States, usually growing in quiet, back waters and on muddy bottoms. The long, ribbonlike leaves are used as food by many animals and the plants serve as substrate for marine algae, Bryozoa, etc.

Figure 158   Figure 159

Fig. 158. *Phyllospadix Scouleri* (Naidaceae) Habit of plant.

Fig. 159. *Zostera marina* (Naidaceae) a. Habit of basal and apical portions of plant; b. Spadix; c. Carpel.

288a. Plants rank, tall stem (up to 2½ M), with long (about 1 M) leaves, up to 20 mm wide, sheathing at the base, the sheath abruptly narrowed at the blade base, bluntly pointed at the apex; inflorescence a double spike composed of numerous staminate flowers above, the pistillate flowers compactly arranged to form a firm cylinder below; plants of shores or emergent in shallow water (not submersed) (Cattail). Fig. 160 ....*Typha*

The familiar cattail is widely distributed over the world, occurring as several species. *T. latifolia* is the most common in this country. It has relatively wide leaves and the terminal staminate spike is in contact with the lower pistillate spike; has multicellular pollen grains. In *T. angustifolia* the leaves are very narrow ribbons; the spikes of flowers are smaller and there is a sterile section of stem appearing between the staminate and pistillate columns. The pollen grains are one-celled. Dense *Typha* stands provide excellent cover for birds and other

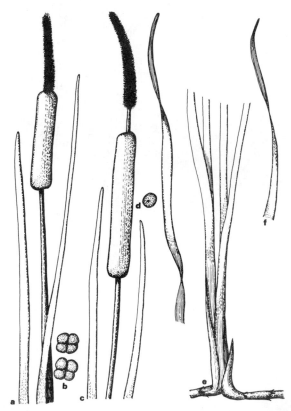

Fig. 160. *Typha* (Typhaeceae) a. *Typha latifolia*, upper portion of leaves and flowering spike; b. Pollen grains; c. *Typha angustifolia*, upper portion of plant showing staminate and pistillate spikes separated; d. Polen; e. Base of plan; f. Leaf tip.

animals. The rhizomes are used by muskrats and beavers, and land mammals sometimes browse on the shoots. Young sprouts and inner parts of the shoots can be used for human food.

288b. Plants shorter, erect and emergent or submersed with long, (up to 2 M) flexible, ribbonlike leaves, emergent leaves up to 4 dm long and erect, flat above but keeled on the back below; the leaves sheathing at the base and with a few alternate on the stem, the sheath gradually narrowed at the blade base (Bur Reed). Fig. 136....................................*Sparganium*

289a. (285) Leaves linear, fleshy and terete or nearly so, relatively short, up to 4 cm long; flowers sometimes solitary but usually several clustered in the axils of leaves; plants stout or somewhat shrubby (Sea Blite). Fig. 161...........................*Suaeda*

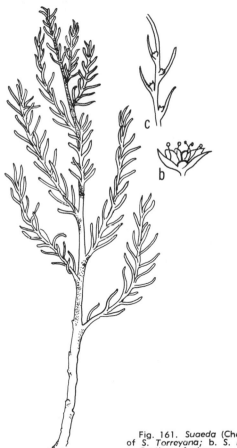

Like so many brackish water and saline plants, the leaves are narrow, fleshy and nearly round. The flowers are solitary or several together in the axils of leaves. There are three species along the coasts of the United States, *Suaeda maritima* occurring on both Atlantic and Pacific shores. *S. depressa* and *S. Torreyana* occur in saline or brackish soils inland.

Fig. 161. *Suaeda* (Chenopodiaceae) a. Habit of *S. Torreyana*; b. *S. linearis*, single flower; c. Section of stem.

Fig. 162. *Carex* (Cyperaceae) a. *Carex stipata*, habit; b. Perigynium; c. Scale; d. Tip of sheath; e. *C. Bebbii*, habit of plant at tip; f. *C. lasiocarpa*, tip of plant; g. Rolled leaf; h. Perigynium; i. *C. comosa*, perigynium and

scale; j. C. *Tuckermannii*, perigynium and scale; k. *C. bullata perigynium* and scale; l. *C. rostrata*, base of plant; m. Tip of plant; n. Perigynium; o. Scale; p. *C. pseudocyperus*, tip of plant; q. Perigynium; r. Scale.

289b. Leaves longer, grasslike, broad at the base and tapering to a point, flat, not terete and fleshy..........................290

290a. Plants submersed; stems lax and drifting but rooted; leaves with parallel veins..291

290b. Plants otherwise...292

291a. Plants with thin leaves that have parallel veins or nerves, and with stipules which are either free or clasping; plants often with broad, floating leaves and in a few species the submersed leaves reduced to quills (Pondweed). Fig. 46..............*Potamogeton*

291b. Plants with thick, sometimes rubbery leaves (often ribbonlike but sometimes grasslike), gradually tapering to a point, without a distinct midrib; stipules lacking; floating leaves wanting (Mud Plantain). Fig. 94...............................*Heteranthera*

292a. (290) *The following genera must be differentiated by type of inflorescence and by characteristics of flower and fruit. Vegetatively they are very similar, with slender, naked stems, or with grasslike, mostly alternate leaves.*

Inflorescence a close cluster of brown flowers appearing to be lateral on an elongated, naked stem, or a cymelike open panicle terminating the stem; flowers composed of 3 brown sepals and petals, 3 or 6 stamens and a superior pistil; leaves slender, alternate on the stem, or as blades arising from a basal sheath (Rush). Fig. 133...............................*Juncus*

292b. Inflorescence various, a headlike cluster or compound raceme, or a simple one, usually with one or more involucral, grasslike leaves; the inflorescence composed of overlapping bracts with florets in the axils, the flower composed of several bristles (or as an inner scale) as a perianth which is sometimes reduced or lacking, with 1 to 3 stamens and 1 pistil bearing a characteristic style according to the genus..........................293

293a. All flowers imperfect, the staminate and pistillate in the same cluster (spike) or in separate spikes on the same plant; the pistil enclosed by a membranous sac (perigynium) (Sedge). Fig. 162 ....*Carex*

Species of *Carex* are solitary or clumped. There are two chief expressions, one in which there are two kinds of flowers intermixed in a terminal spike, and a group in which the staminate spikes (above) are separate from the pistillate spikes (below). The genus is peculiar in having the ovary inclosed in a variously shaped sac called the perigynium. The many species are marginal, occurring in marshes and wet meadows, and along shores. *C. lasiocarpa* is an important builder of soil in bogs and bays, speeding the ageing of lakes.

293b. **Flowers all perfect, or sometimes with perfect flowers and some with stamens only in the same spike**.....................294

294a. **Inflorescence a single spikelet, terminal on a long, naked stem.**
....295

294b. **Inflorescence not as above**..............................297

295a. **Spikelet terminal oval, elliptic or nearly round, with flower bristles inconspicuous or absent; culms angular or round in cross section (Spike Rush). Fig. 134**................*Eleocharis*

295b. **Bristles conspicuous, long and silky, often white or tawny**....296

296a. **Bristles numerous, silky and white (becoming tawny), smooth (Cotton Grass). Fig. 140**.........................*Eriophorum*

296b. **Bristles at the base of the nutlet few (1 to 8), or none, barbed (rarely smooth in some species), white and silky, nutlets (achenes) elongate (Alpine Cotton Grass). Fig. 163**.............
....*Scirpus hudsonianus*
This species resembles *Eriophorum* and at times has been classified there. The bristles are relatively few in number (about 4) and are toothed. Plants are well-named Cotton Grass; occur in *Sphagnum* bogs and wet meadows.

297a. **(294) Stems solid, triangular in cross section (sometimes with rounded angles)**...298

297b. **Stems hollow, round in cross section, often leafy with grasslike leaves arising on 3 sides of the stem, one at each node; inflorescence terminal and also axilary (Three-way-Sedge) Fig. 164**
....*Dulichium*
This sedge has a hollow stem that is practically round in cross section and one which bears a short, grasslike leaf at almost every node. Flowers arise in a terminal raceme as well as in smaller, axillary racemes. Plants are important as beach-builders; are used sparsely by birds and muskrats.

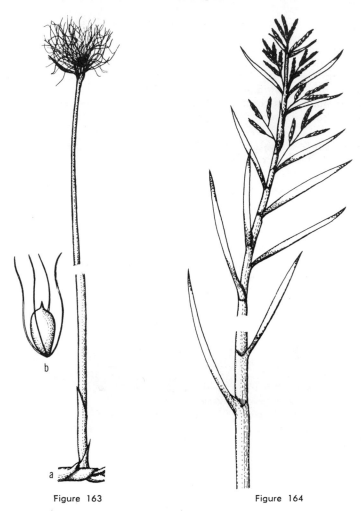

Figure 163   Figure 164

Fig. 163. *Scirpus hudsonianus* (Cyperaceae) a. Habit; b. Nutlet and bristles.

Fig. 164. *Dulichium arundinaceum* (Cyperaceae) Habit of plant tip.

298a. Scales of the spikelet borne in 2 distinct rows, the spikelet accordingly flattened (Sedge). Fig. 156..................*Cyperus*

298b. Scales of the spikelet arising from all sides of the axis, the
spikelet in general rounded in cross section................299

299a. Spikelets many-flowered.................................300

299b. Spikelet with only 1 or 2 flowers, with several of the lower
scales sterile...301

300a. Leaf above the spikelets round in cross section, appearing as a continuation of the stem; achene lacking a tubercle; lowermost scales of the spikelet only sterile (Bulrush). Fig. 132..........
....*Scirpus americanus*

300b. Leaf or leaves above the spikelets not round in cross section, but grasslike, with blades tapering to a point; leaves below the spikelets sometimes appearing to be whorled (Bulrush). Fig. 132 c,d..*Scirpus* spp.

301a. Achenes lacking a tubercle and with no basal bristles about the achene (Twig Rush). Fig. 165......................*Cladium*

Figure 165   Figure 166

Fig. 165. *Cladium* (Cyperaceae) a. *Cladium mariscoides*, habit of plant; b. spikelet.

Fig. 166. *Rynchospora* (Cyperaceae) a. *Rynchospora alba*, habit of upper portion of stem; b. Nutlet; c. *R. macrostachya*, habit of stem tip; d. Nutlet.

This plant has cylindrical spikelets with only the uppermost bearing flowers. Stems are usually leafy and may be as much as 1 M tall. They bear a much-branched inflorescence with several spikelets on each branch. *C. mariscoides* is the most common species throughout most of the eastern half of the United States. There is no known biological importance.

301b. Achene with a prominent tubercle of various forms, subtended by bristles; spikelets with empty scales below the fertile ones, the spikelets often densely clustered to form heads (Beak Rush). Fig. 166...Rynchospora

The Beak Rush is well-named because the nutlet bears a prominent tubercle. The spikelet cluster has several leafy involucres which appear as a whorl. *R. macrostachya* is a common member of a *Sphagnum* bog flora, usually standing above the other vegetation and showing the spikelets in dense clumps. The tubercles may be as much as 2.2 cm long.

SELECTED LIST OF USEFUL REFERENCES

Arber, Agnes. 1920. Water plants. (Reprinted 1963 by J. Cramer, Weinheim.)

Benson, Lyman. 1957. Plant classification. Heath and Company. Boston, Mass.

Daubs, E. H. 1965. A monograph of Lemnaceae. Univ. of Illinois Press, Urbana, Ill.

Fassett, F. N. 1940. A manual of aquatic plants. McGraw-Hill Book Co., New York. (Reprinted 1966 by Univ. of Wisconsin Press. Madison, Wis.)

Fernald, M. L. 1950. Gray's manual of botany. American Book Co. New York.

Gleason, H. A. and Cronquist, Arthur. 1963. Manual of vascular plants of northeastern United States and adjacent Canada. Van Nostrand Co. New York.

Marie-Victorin, Frère. 1947. Flore Laurentienne. Montréal, Canada.

Martin, A. C. and Uhler, F. M. 1951. Food of game ducks in the United States and Canada. U.S.D.A. Technical Bulletin No. 634. 1939. (Reprinted as Research Report No. 30, Fish and Wildlife Service, U.S. Dept. of the Interior, 1951).

Martin, A. C., Zim, H. E. and Nelson, A. L. 1951. American wildlife and plants. McGraw-Hill Book Co. New York.

Mason, H. L. 1957. A flora of the marshes of California. Univ. California Press. Berkeley, Calif.

Muenscher, W. C. 1944. Aquatic plants of the United States. Comstock. Ithaca, N.Y.

Peck, M. E. 1941. A manual of the higher plants of Oregon. Binfords and Mort. Portland, Ore.

Sculthorpe, C. D. 1967. The biology of aquatic vascular plants. St. Martin's Press. New York.

Steward, A. N., Dennis, L. J. and Gilkey, Helen M. 1963. Aquatic plants of the Pacific Northwest. Oregon State Univ. Press. Corvallis, Ore.

CHECK LIST OF AQUATIC PLANT GENERA AND THEIR FAMILY CLASSIFICATION(*)

(For reference the family names are arranged alphabetically within their respective major plant groups.)

RHODOPHYTA
Batrachospermaceae
Batrachospermum
Fig. 12, p. 15
CHLOROPHYTA
Cladophoraceae
Cladophora
Fig. 13, p. 15
Characeae
Chara
Fig. 9, p. 12
Nitella
Fig. 10, p. 13
Tolypella
Fig. 11, p. 14
BRYOPHYTA
HEPATICAE
Harpanthaceae
Chiloscyphus
Fig. 15, p. 17
Marchantiaceae
Conocephalum
Fig. 2, p. 8
Marchantia
Fig. 1, p. 7
Ricciaceae
Riccia
Fig. 7, p. 11
Ricciocarpus
Fig. 8, p. 11
MUSCI
Bartramiaceae
*Philonotis**
Fissidentaceae
Fissidens
Fig. 17, p. 18
Fontinalaceae
Fontinalis
Fig. 16, p. 17
Hypnaceae
Drepanocladus
Fig. 18, p. 19
Sphagnaceae
Sphagnum
Fig. 14, p. 16
PTERIDOPHYTA
Equisetaceae
Equisetum
Fig. 123, p. 115
Isoetaceae
Isoetes
Fig. 147, p. 134
Marsileaceae
Marsilea
Fig. 106, p. 99
Osmundaceae
Osmunda
Fig. 104, p. 97
Parkeriaceae
Ceratopteris
Fig. 87, p. 83
Polypodiaceae
*Onoclea**

Salviniaceae
Azolla
Fig. 19, p. 19
Salvinia
Fig. 20, p. 20

SPERMATOPHYTA
GYMNOSPERMAE
Pinaceae
Larix
Fig. 21, p. 21
Picea
Taxodium
Fig. 22, p. 22

ANGIOSPERMAE
Monocotyledonae
Alismaceae
Alisma
Fig. 102, p. 95
Damasonium
Fig. 101, p. 95
Echinodorus
Fig. 96, p. 90
Lophotocarpus
Fig. 93, p. 88
Sagittaria
Fig. 92, p. 87
Araceae
Acorus
Fig. 139, p. 130
Calla
Fig. 69, p. 67
Lysichitum
Fig. 100, p. 94
Orontium
Fig. 103, p. 97
Peltandra
Fig. 91, p. 86
Pistia
Fig. 86, p. 82
Symplocarpus
Fig. 99, p. 94
Butomaceae
Butomus
Fig. 145, p. 133
Cyperaceae
Carex
Fig. 162, pp. 148-149
Cladium
Fig. 165, p. 153
Cyperus
Fig. 156, p. 142
Dulichium
Fig. 164, p. 152
Eleocharis
Fig. 134, p. 125
Eriophorum
Fig. 140, p. 130
Rynchospora
Fig. 166, p. 153
Scirpus
Fig. 132, p. 123
Fig. 141, p. 132
Fig. 163, p. 152

(*) Names marked with * are not included in the Key.

157

APPENDIX

APPENDIX

INDEX AND PICTURED-GLOSSARY

CYME: a flat-topped cluster of flowers in which the central flowers are the oldest. Fig. 179

Figure 179

Cyperaceae, 123, 125, 130, 132, 142, 151, 152
Cyperus, 142, 151
  esculenta, 142
Cypress, 22

D

Damasonium, 95, 96
  californicum, 95
Darlingtonia californica, 30
DECIDUOUS: falling away at the end of the growing season, or not retained throughout the life of the organism; temporary.
Decodon, 24, 36, 53
  verticillatum, 24
Delta Potato, 87, 96, 127
DELTOID: shaped as the Greek letter D; triangular. Fig. 180

Figure 180

DENTATE: toothed, as a dentate leaf margin. Fig. 181

Figure 181

DENTICULATE: with small (u s u a l l y numerous) teeth. Fig. 182

Figure 182

Dermatocarpon, 7
Dianthera, 52, 53, 140
  americana, 52
  ovata, 53
DICHOTOMOUS: dividing, sometimes repeatedly, in two, usually e q u a l parts.
Fig. 183

Figure 183

Dicotyledonae, viii, 1
Didiplis, 139, 140
  diandra, 140
  linearis, 139, 140
DIOECIOUS: with two sorts of spores, or with two sexes appearing on separate plants
DISC FLOWER: the inner, tubular flowers of a head as in the Compositae
DISSECTED: with deep divisions; deeply cut into separate parts. Fig. 184

Figure 184

Distribution, 2
DIVIDED: incisions to the base; deeply cut into separate parts. Fig. 185

Figure 185

Division (Phylum), 1
Dock, 75, 82
DORSAL: referring to the back; the top side as opposed to the under or ventral surface.
DORSIVENTRAL: a thallus or plant part showing a difference between top and bottom.
Dogwood, 27, 28
  Red Ozier, 27
Drepanocladus, 19, 115
Dropwort, 111, 122
Drosera, 85
  linearis, 85
  rotundifolia, 85
Droseraceae, 85
Drying Plants, 5
Duckweed, 9, 111
  Great, 9, 20, 43, 111
  Star, 112
  Strap-shaped, 10
Dulichium, 150
  arundinaceum, 151

E

Echinodorus, 91, 96, 97
  cordifolius, 90
Economic Importance, vii, 16, 20, 25, 31, 115, 123
Eel Grass, 145
Eichhornia crassipes, 84
Elatinaceae, 50
Elatine, 50, 53, 114
  americana, 51
  triandra, 50
Eleocharis, 124, 150, also 29
  albida, 125
  obtusa, 125
  palustris, 125
  Robbinsii, 124
ELLIPSOID: like an ellipse; elliptic. Fig. 186

Figure 186

INDEX

GLUME: a bract at the base of a grass spikelet. Fig. 194

Figure 194

Figure 195

INCISED: with sharp cuts along a margin, sometimes deep. Fig. 196

Figure 196

I

IMBRICATE: overlapping as in bud scales, or overlapping of leaves on a stem. Fig. 195

INFERIOR OVARY: an ovary below other flower parts; with the perianth attached to the top of the ovary.
INTERNODE: a section of a stem axis between nodes or joints.
INVOLUCRE: scales, bracts or leaves subtending reproductive flower parts, or subtending a group of flowers.

J

JOINT: a section or portion; a unit of a thallus. Fig. 197

Figure 197

K

L

LANCEOLATE: lance-shaped; narrowly elliptic and tapering at both ends. Fig. 198

Figure 198

LEMMA: one of the two scales about the reproductive parts of a grass flower, the other being the palea. Fig. 199. Text Figure 1

Figure 199

165

INDEX

LIGULE: a thin scale or membrane across the base of a leaf at the top of the sheath (base of the blade) in the grass family. Fig. 200

Figure 200

Lilaea subulata, 137
Liliaceae, 133
Limnobium, 83, 91
  spongia, 83
Limosella, 93, 134, 136
  aquatica, 93
  subulata, 93
Lindernia, 56
  anagallidea, 57
  dubia, 57
LINEAR: a narrow and elongate leaf or lobe, several times longer than broad with parallel or subparallel margins usually. Fig. 201

Figure 201

Lippia, 62
  lanceolata, 62
  nodiflora, 62
Littorella, 128, 135
  americana, 128
Liverworts, viii, 7, 17
LOBE: a part extended from the whole; a segment.
Lobelia, 77, 85
  cardinalis, 77
  Dortmanna, 77
Lobeliaceae, 77
Loosestrife, 41, 52, 53, 79
Lophotocarpus, 88
Lotus, 32
Ludwigia, 49, 53, 79, 81
  linearis, 49
  palustris, 49
  polycarpa, 49

Luzula, 124
Lycopsida, viii
Lycopus, 64, 65
  americana, 54, 65
Lysichitum americanum, 94
Lysimachia, 41, 52, 53, 79
  ciliata, 41
  terrestris, 42
  thyrsiflora, 41, 42, 52
Lythraceae, 24, 42, 52, 139, 141
Lythrum, 42, 51, 53, 54, 79
  alatum, 42
  lineare, 51
  Salicaria, 42

M

Macuillamia, 59
Manatee, 84
Manna Grass, 119
Marchantia polymorpha, 7, 8
Marchantiaceae, 8
Marsh Marigold, 67, 81, 91
Marsilea, 99, 100
  quadrifolia, 99
  vestita, 99
Marsileaceae, 99
Mayaca, 114
Mayocaceae, 114
Megalodonta, 61, 70, 109
  Beckii, 61
Mentha, 64, 65
  arvensis, 64
  piperata, 64
  spicata, 64
Menyanthaceae, 34, 98
Menyanthes, trifoliata, 98
Mermaid Weed, 74, 82, 102
Milfoil, 109, 111, 113
Mimulus, 56, 58, 59, 60
  alatus, 56
  guttatus, 56
  Lewisii, 56
  moschatus, 56
  ringens, 56
Mint, 64
Monkey Flower, 56, 59, 60
Monocotyledonae, viii, 1
MONOECIOUS: with two kinds of spores, or with two sexes on the same plant, but in separate reproductive structures.
Mosses 11, 17, 18, 19, 114
Mounting Plants, 5
Mud Plantain, 89, 96, 126, 148
Mudwort, 93, 134, 136
Musci, viii
Muskgrass, 12
Myosotis, 77, 78
  scorpoides, 77
Myriophyllum, 109, 111, also 2, 108
  exalbescens, 108
  tenellum, 109, 113
  verticillatum, 108

N

Naiadaceae, 44, 54, 136, 138, 146
Naias, 138, 139, 142
  flexilis, 138
Nasturtium, 72, 76, 102
  officinale, 72

Nelumbo, 32
  lutea, 33
Neobeckia, 70, 81, 108, also 61
  aquatica, 70
NERVES: thin veins; a thin rib.
Nightshade, 73, 76
Nitella, 2, 13
NODE: a section of a stem or axis which bears branches or leaves as in the Characeae. Fig. 9. Fig. 202

Figure 202

NUCULE: a s p e c i a l i z e d branch which forms a globular or oval body in which an oogonium is borne in the Characeae. Fig. 9
Nuphar, 34, 35, 66, also 1
  advena, 34, also 1
  polysepala, 1
  variegatum, 34, also 1
NUTLET: a small, dry fruit as an achene (q.v.)
Nutrients, 2
Nymphaea, 35, 66, also 1, 2
  odorata, 35, also 1
  tetragona, 35
  tuberosa, 35, also 1
Nymphaeaceae, 1, 31, 32, 35
Nymphoides, 34
  cordatum, 34
  peltatum, 34

O

OBLANCEOLATE: a figure (leaf, e.g.) broader toward the apex and more sharply narrowed toward the base. Fig. 203

Figure 203

INDEX

OBLONG: a figure (leaf, e.g.) oval but with broadly rounded ends and subparallel margins: Fig. 204

Figure 204

Oenanthe, 104, also 2
  sarmentosa, 104
Onagraceae, 37, 49, 78
ORBICULAR: nearly round; approximately globular.
Order, defined, 1
Orontium, 96, 97
  aquaticum, 97
Osmunda regalis, 97
Osmundaceae, 97
OVAL: elongated, circular figure, broadly rounded at either pole. Fig. 205

Figure 205

Oxygen Relationships, 2
Oxypolis, 103, 104, 111, 122
  occidentale, 103

P

PALEA: one of two scales about the reproductive parts of a grass flower, the other being the lemma. Text Figure 1
PALMATE: with divisions radiating from a common point (as lobes of a leaf or veins of a leaf). Fig. 206

Figure 206

PANICLE: a loose cluster of flowers as in the grass inflorescence. Fig. 127, 207

Figure 207

Parkeriaceae, 83
Parrot Feather, 31, 36, 46, 106, 109
PEDICEL: a flower stalk, the stem which bears the flower.
PEDUNCLE: a flowering stem which may bear several pedicels and their individual flowers.
Peltandra, 86, 91
  virginica, 86
PELTATE: shieldlike, as a leaf with the petiole attached in the center of the blade.
Peplis diandra, 140
Pepperwort, 99, 100
PERFECT FLOWER: a flower containing both pistil and stamens.
PERIANTH: the involucre of a flower; the sterile parts about the reproductive elements, composed of both petals and sepals or only one of these series.

Figure 208

PERIGYNIUM: a flasklike covering of the nutlet in the genus Carex. Fig. 209

Figure 209

PETIOLE: the stalk of a leaf, bearing one or more blades.
Phaeophyta, viii
Phalaris arundinacea, 118
PHOTOTROPISM: response or movement in the direction of light source.
Phragmites maximus, 117
Phycoerythrin, the red pigment found in Rhodophyta.
PHYLLODE: a bladeless leaf petiole
PHYLLODIA: a leaf reduced to a petiole, without a blade. Fig. 210

Figure 210

Phyllospadix Scouleri, 144, 145
Physostegia virginiana, 60
Picea mariana, 21
Pickerelweed, 90, 96
Pigmy Weed, 50, 114
Pinaceae, 21, 22
PINNATE: like a feather; a compound leaf with leaflets arranged along an axis; lobings featherlike. Fig. 211

Figure 211

Pipewort, 133, 137
Pistia stratioides, 82
PISTIL: the female reproductive part of a flower including an ovary, style (usually present as a slender stalk) and a stigma (pollen receiver).
Pitcher Plant, 21, 29, 30
Plantaginaceae, 128
POD: a dry, many-seeded fruit such as in the pea family. See Silique.
Podostemaceae, 100
Podostemum, 100, 143, also 2, 29
  ceratophyllum, 100

167

Q

R

Figure 212

cence around the central, tubular flowers; sometimes the entire head composed of petal-like flowers as in Dandelion).

Figure 213

REVOLUTE: with enrolled margins.
RHIZOID: a fine hairlike extension of a cell forming an anchoring or absorbing organ.
RHIZOME: a thick, horizontal underground stem.
Rhodophyta, viii
RHOMBOID: somewhat quadrangular with rounded angles.
ROOTSTOCK: a thickened basal part of a plant with rootlike characters.
ROTATE: circular; disclike. Fig. 214

Figure 214

S

SAGGITATE: arrow-shaped.
SALVERFORM: a v-shaped tube with a broadened, rotate opening. Fig. 215

Figure 215

SCAPE: a flowering shoot (usually without leaves) arising from a basal position.
SERRATE: sharply toothed along the margin. Fig. 216

INDEX

Figure 216

SHEATH: a thin (usually) membranous expansion of a petiole base which encloses the stem wholly or in part; a scalelike collar which surrounds the stem at the nodes.

SHEATHING: one leaf partly enclosing another at their bases; a leaf base partly or wholly enclosing a stem.

SICKLE-SHAPED: s h a r p l y crescent-shaped.

SILIQUE: the podfruit of the mustard family consisting of two (usually) chambers (locules), the t w o parts separating from a central axis at maturity. Fig. 217

Figure 217

SPADIX: a flowering shoot, usually thick, bearing a compact head or cylinder of many small flowers, usually enclosed by a broad sheath, the spathe (q.v.) Fig. 218

SPATHE: a broad involucral scale or a membranous

envelope about a spadix (q.v.). Fig. 218

Figure 218

SPATULATE: a figure (leaf) decidedly broader and rounded at the apex, narrowing toward the base. Fig. 219

Figure 219

SPIKE: a straight, stout inflorescence with flowers closely arranged along the axis at the apex of the stem or lateral shoot.

SPIKELET: a branch of a spike; a small portion of an inflorescence bearing a few (or only one) flowers; see grasses and sedges. Fig. 220

Figure 220

SPORANGIOPHORE: a stem branch, or a stalk which bears sporangia, the sporangiophores usually arranged to form a cone or strobilus as in Equisetum and the Lycopsida.

SPOROCARP: a nutlike body including several sporangia (a covered sorus) as in Salvinia and Marsilea. Fig. 221

Figure 221

STIGMA: the pollen-collecting surface of a pistil.

STIPULE: a winglike or scalelike organ attached to the base of a leaf petiole or on the stem at the point of leaf attachment; the stipule sometimes taking the form of a thorn. Fig. 222

Figure 222

SUCCULENT: t h i c k a n d fleshy, swollen and often juicy.

Figure 223

Figure 224

Figure 225

Figure 226

Figure 227

Figure 228

Figure 229